Building Construction

Project Management, Construction Administration, Drawings, Specs, Detailing Tips, Schedules, Checklists, and Secrets Others Don't Tell You (Architectural Practice Simplified, 2nd edition)

GANG CHEN

ArchiteG®, Inc.
Irvine, California

Building Construction:
Project Management, Construction Administration, Drawings, Specs, Detailing Tips, Schedules, Checklists, and Secrets Others Don't Tell You
(Architectural Practice Simplified, 2nd edition)

Copyright © 2010 Gang Chen
V1.0
Cover Photo © 2010 Gang Chen

ArchiteG®, Inc.
http://www.ArchiteG.com

ISBN: 978-0-9843741-4-4

Dedication

To my parents, Zhuixian and Yugen,
my wife, Xiaojie, and my daughters,
Alice, Angela, Amy, and Athena.

Disclaimer

Building Construction (or *Architectural Practice Simplified,* 2nd edition) provides general information about building construction and architectural practice. The book is sold with the understanding that neither the publisher nor the author is providing legal, accounting, or other professional services. If legal, accounting, or other professional services are required, seek the assistance of a competent professional firm.

The purpose of this publication is not to reprint the content of all other available texts on the subject. You are urged to read other materials, and tailor them to fit your needs.

Great effort has been taken to make this resource as complete and accurate as possible; however, nobody is perfect, and there may be several typographical errors or other mistakes present. You should use this book as a general guide and not as the ultimate source on this subject. If you find any potential errors, please send an e-mail to:
info@ArchiteG.com

Building Construction is intended to provide general, entertaining, informative, educational, and enlightening content. Neither the publisher nor the author shall be liable to anyone or any entity for any loss or damages, or alleged loss and damages, caused directly or indirectly by the content of this book.

All firm names, addresses, and contact information used in the book are fictitious, for demonstration purposes only.

Table of Contents

Chapter One   From Architectural Schools to Architectural Practice

A. A Cultural Shock...**15**
   1. Why Do I Still Feel Like an Idiot in an Architectural Office, Even Though I Just Got My Architectural Degree from a Top Architectural School?
   2. What Went Wrong?

B. The Roles of an Architect...**16**
   1. Architect as a **Specialist**
   2. Architect as a **Generalist**

C. Abbreviations and Technical Terms..**17**
   Sample Abbreviation List for Building and Site

D. Office Libraries & Most Commonly Used Books in Architectural Offices...........**20**
   1. **Design Library**
      Product Catalogs and Samples; the **Holistic Design Concept** and Several Architecture, Planning, and Landscape Books to Help You **Overcome "the Designer Block"**

   2. **General Library**
      a. **Codes, Acts and Regulations**
         American with Disabilities Act (**ADA**); **Title 24**, *California Disabled Accessibility Guidebook* (**CalDAG**) & *California Accessibility Reference Manual Code & Checklist* (**CARM**); *International Building Code* (**IBC**) and Its Local Adaptations; Other International Code Council (**ICC**) Codes; *National Electrical Code* (**NEC**); Municipal Codes; *Building Codes Illustrated*

      b. **Reference Books**
         The Steel Book; LEED Reference Guides and Documents; *Architectural Graphic Standards; Building Construction Illustrated*

c. **AIA and Commonly Used AIA Forms**
A-Series; B-Series; C-Series; D-Series; E-Series; G-Series; Free AIA Documents for Download; Commonly Used AIA Forms

d. **CSI MasterFormat, *Sweets Catalog*, and Various Manufacturers' Product Catalogs**
Comparing Old and New Version of MasterFormat

e. **Computer-Aided Design & Drafting & Other CADD Books**

3. **Commonly Used Manufacturers' & Various Websites**
Masonry (**Full Bricks & Thin Bricks**); Masonry Institute of America (**MIA**); Pacific Clay Products, Inc; Coronado Stone; Eldorado Stone; Cultured Stone; Wood and Plastic Fastenings; Simpson StrongTie; Thermal Protection: **Batt Insulation and Rigid Insulation**; Johns Manville; **Roof Tiles: Concrete Roof Tile** and **Clay Roof Tile**; Eagle Roofing; MonierLifetile (MLT); MCA Superior Clay Roof Tile; Membrane Roofing: **Bituminous Systems & Single-Ply Roofing Systems**; Firestone Building Products; GAF Materials Corporation; Entrances and Storefronts: ¼" **Thick** Glazing or **1" Insulated** Glazing; Kawneer Products; U.S. Aluminum Commercial Products Group; Arcadia, Inc; Special Wall Surfacing: FRP/Marlite; **Sweets Network;** Portland Cement Association; Fry Reglet Architectural Metals

Chapter Two   Clients and Contracts

Chapter Five   **Construction Documents (CD)**

3. Coordination of Construction Drawings
    a. Coordination of Structural Drawings
    b. Coordination of Electrical Drawings
    c. Coordination of Mechanical Drawings
    d. Coordination of Plumbing Drawings
    e. Coordination of Architectural Sheets
       Note: Each item above includes <u>Sheet-by-Sheet</u> Checklists.

Chapter Six   Bidding & Negotiation

Chapter Seven   **Construction Administration**

Chapter Eight   **Collections**

Appendixes

1. **List of Tables**
2. **Definition of Architects and Some Important Information about Architects and the Profession of Architecture**
3. **AIA Compensation Survey**
4. **So ... You would Like to Study Architecture**
5. **Annotated Bibliography**

Back page promotion

1. *Planting Design Illustrated*
2. **LEED Exam Guides series**
   (ArchiteG.com)

Chapter One

From Architectural Schools to Architectural Practice

A. A Cultural Shock

1. Why Do I Still Feel Like an Idiot in an Architectural Office, Even Though I Just Got My Architectural Degree from a Top Architectural School?

You just spent 5 years of your life in college and two hundred thousand dollars on your tuition, and finally you graduated from a top architectural school. You just got a new job at a good architectural firm, and all a sudden, you realize that what you learned at school does NOT seem to help you at work AT ALL, and people at work talk in a language that you barely understand: Entitlement, RFI, Shop Drawings, CCD, Change Order, Punch List, etc. You feel like an idiot in your office and do not seem to know anything. This is a total cultural shock to you.

2. What Went Wrong?

Well, there is a **huge gap** between architectural education and architectural practice.

a. When you are in architectural school, design courses mainly teach you conceptual design. In the real world of architectural practice, **conceptual design is only a very small portion of the design process.** All the real projects will go through many phases, including Entitlement, Conceptual Design/Schematic Design, Design Development, Construction Document, Bidding and Negotiation, Construction Administration, and sometimes even Operation and Maintenance.

b. In the real world, employees in an architectural firm are put in one of three categories: **supporting staff (including administrative, marketing, and IT or CADD), designers, and management and production staff.** If you are hired as a designer, you will have an easier transition from college to your job because a designer mainly deals with Entitlement, Conceptual Design/Schematic Design, and sometimes, Design Development work. If you are hired as a production employee, you will have a much harder transition, because almost everything you do in the office is what you have almost NEVER dealt with in school before. You will have to learn on-the-job.

c. In college, the knowledge you learned is **piecemeal in nature**: you learn structure as one course, and architectural history as another, and design studio is yet another, and so on. In the real world of architectural practice, you can be dealing with all these elements in one single project, and you need to be able to integrate the knowledge you learned from different courses and create a **synergy**.

Synergy is defined as the working together of two things to produce an effect greater than the sum of their individual effects.

To help you make a smooth and easy transition from architectural school to architectural practice, I summarize my professional experience and tips in this book, which should be useful to readers.

There are many, many things that you need to learn to work well in the real world of architectural practice, but **there are only a certain number of tips that you need to know to be able to function and survive in the daily operation of an architectural firm or in the construction industry.** In this book, we shall cover all the basic and pragmatic knowledge to help you handle the daily workload in an architectural office, and we shall tell you where you can find further information.

B. The Roles of an Architect

There are two basic roles that an architect needs to play: a specialist and a generalist.

1. Architect as a Specialist

First, an architect is a specialist, and you need to have thorough and in-depth knowledge on architecture: you need to know architectural history, how to do sketch and perspective, and how to read and draw plans, elevations, sections, details, etc.

2. Architect as a Generalist

Second, an architect is a generalist or a "general contractor" for design service.

Many consultants, such as structural, electrical, mechanical, and plumbing engineers are design "subcontractors," and they subcontract a portion of the design work under the architect's master design contract.

Some other consultants such as soils, civil and fire protection engineers, and landscape architects are typically under the owner's contract. (They could be under the architect's contract also, depending on how the master design contract is structured.)

Regardless whose contract these consultants are under, as an architect, a generalist for design work, you do need to know enough about their portion of the work to coordinate them.

C. Abbreviations and Technical Terms

There are some abbreviations and technical terms that are commonly used in architectural offices. They are listed below for your convenience. You can read through the list, make a mental note of the information and where to locate it in the book, and you can MEMORIZE the information by reading this book multiple times instead of using the "mechanical" memory.

One way to do this is to cover the full technical terms and see if you can tell the correct answer from the abbreviations. If you get a correct answer, then you can move on to the next one. If you cannot tell the correct answer, then highlight it with a highlighter. The next time you read the book, you can focus on the highlighted ones. This will save you a great deal of time, because you are focusing on your weakness.

Once you are familiar with these basic vocabularies, abbreviations, and technical terms, you will feel more comfortable in reading plans and other paperwork, or engaging in a conversation in an architectural office.

These terms are often compiled as a list of abbreviations and placed on the cover sheet of a set of construction documents. Some abbreviations may have more than one meaning, and you need to understand their context to figure out the correct meaning.

I place this list at the front of this book instead of in the appendixes because I want you to pay attention to these terms and become familiar with them. They are important.

Here is the list:

Table 1.1   Sample Abbreviation List for Building and Site:

Abbreviations	Meaning	Abbreviations	Meaning
A.	ALLOWANCE	H.M.	HOLLOW METAL
A.B.	ANCHOR BOLT	HORIZ.	HORIZONTAL
A/C	AIR CONDITIONING	HT.	HEIGHT
A.C.	ASPHALTIC CONCRETE	I.D.	INSIDE DIAMETER
A.C.T.	ACOUSTICAL CEILING TILE	INSUL.	INSULATION
A.F.F.	ABOVE FINISH FLOOR	INT.	INTERIOR
ALT.	ALTERNATE	JAN.	JANITOR
ALUM.	ALUMINUM	JBS.	JAMBS
APPR.	APPROXIMATE	JT.	JOINT
A.R.	ARCHITECTURAL REPRESENTATIVE	LAM.	LAMINATE
A.S.R.	AUTOMATIC SPRINKLER RISER	LAV.	LAVATORY
BD.	BOARD	MAX.	MAXIMUM
BLK.	BLOCK	MECH.	MECHANICAL

BLDG.	BUILDING	M.H.	MANHOLE
BLKG.	BLOCKING	MIN.	MINIMUM
BM.	BEAM	MISC.	MISCELLANEOUS
BOT.	BOTTOM	M.O.	MASONRY OPENING
C.B.	CATCH BASIN	MTD.	MOUNTED
C.D.	CRITICAL DIMENSION +/- ½" F.O.F., OR CONSTRUCTION DOCUMENTS	MTL.	METAL
C.J.	CONTROL JOINT	MTR.	METER
C.L.	CENTER LINE	NIC/ N.I.C.	NOT IN CONTRACT
CLG.	CEILING	NO.	NUMBER
CLR.	CLEAR	N.L.T.	NOT LESS THAN
C.M.	CONSTRUCTION MANAGER	N.T.S.	NOT TO SCALE
C.M.U.	CONCRETE MASONRY UNITS	O/	OVER
C.O.	CLEAN OUT	O.C.	ON CENTER
CONC.	CONCRETE	O.D.	OUTSIDE DIAMETER/OVERFLOW DRAIN
CONT.	CONTINUOUS	O.F.L.	OVERFLOW LEADER
CONTR.	CONTRACTOR	O.H.	OVERHEAD
COL.	COLUMN	OPNG.	OPENING
C.R.	CONSTRUCTION REPRESENTATIVE	OPP.	OPPOSITE
C.T.	CERAMIC TILE	OPP. HD.	OPPOSITE HAND
CTR.	CENTER	O.S.	OVERFLOW SCUPPER
DBL.	DOUBLE	O.S.B.	ORIENTED STRAND BOARD
D.F.	DRINKING FOUNTAIN	P.B.C.	PLUMBING CONTRACTOR
DIA.	DIAMETER	P.I.V.	POST INDICATOR VALVE
DN.	DOWN	PL.	PLATE
DR.	DOOR	P.L.	PROPERTY LINE
D.S.	DOWNSPOUT	PLAS. LAM.	PLASTIC LAMINATE
DTL./ DET.	DETAIL	PLYWD.	PLYWOOD
DWG.	DRAWING	P.O.C.	POINT OF CONNECTION
EA.	EACH	PR.	PAIR
E.D.F.	ELECTRIC DRINKING FOUNTAIN	PT.	PAINT
E.F.	EXHAUST FAN	RAD.	RADIUS

E.C.	ELECTRICAL CONTRACTOR	R.D.	RAIN DRAIN
ELEC. / ELECT.	ELECTRICAL	R.D.L.	RAIN DRAIN LEADER
ELEV.	ELEVATION	REINF.	REINFORCED
EQ.	EQUAL	REQ'D.	REQUIRED
EQUIP.	EQUIPMENT	RESIL.	RESILIENT
ETC.	ETCETERA	RM.	ROOM
E.W.	EACH WAY	R.O.	ROUGH OPENING
EWC/ E.W.C.	ELECTRIC WATER COOLER	S.C.	SOLID CORE
EXIST.	EXISTING	SHTG.	SHEATHING
EXP.	EXPANSION/EXPOSED	SIM.	SIMILAR
F.B.O.	FURNISHED BY OTHERS	SPECS./ SPEC.	SPECIFICATIONS
FD/F.D.	FLOOR DRAIN	SQ.	SQUARE
F.F.	FINISH FLOOR	S.S.	SANITARY SERVICE
F.G.	FINISH GRADE	STD	STANDARD
F.H.	FIRE HYDRANT	STL.	STEEL
FIN.	FINISH(ED)	STRUCT	STRUCTURAL
FLR.	FLOOR	T.O.	TOP OF
F.O.C.	FACE OF CONCRETE	T.O.C.	TOP OF CON-CRETE/TOP OF CURB
F.O.F.	FACE OF FINISH	T.O.M.	TOP OF MASONRY
F.O.M.	FACE OF MASONRY	T.O.S.	TOP OF STEEL
F.O.S.	FACE OF STUD	T.O.P.	TOP OF PARAPET
F.P.	FIREPROOF/FIRE PROTEC-TION	T.S.	TUBE STEEL/TOP OF SHEATHING
F.S.	FLOOR SINK/FINISH SUR-FACE	TYP.	TYPICAL
FTG.	FOOTING	U.N.O.	UNLESS NOTED OTH-ERWISE
FURR.	FURRING	U.O.N.	UNLESS OTHERWISE NOTED
GA.	GAUGE	V.C.T.	VINYL COMPOSITION TILE
GALV.	GALVANIZED	V.	VERIFY
GC/G.C.	GENERAL CONTRACTOR	V.I.F.	VERIFY IN FIELD
G.I.	GALVANIZED IRON	VL/V.L.	VERIFY LOCATION
GL.	GLASS/GLAZING	W/	WITH
G.W.B.	GYPSUM WALL BOARD	W/O	WITHOUT
G.V.	GRAVITY VENTILATOR	WD.	WOOD
GYP.	GYPSUM	W.H.	WATER HEATER
GYP. BD.	GYPSUM BOARD		
H.C.	HOLLOW CORE	WTR.	WATER

D. Office Libraries & Most Commonly Used Books in Architectural Offices

Most offices have at least two libraries: a Design Library & a General Library. The **design library** is often placed in a room that is close to the design department and has natural light because the designers will need to see the true colors of product samples in **natural light.**

The **general library** can be placed next to the design library, but most of the time, it is placed in the same room as the copier. These libraries will typically have the following content:

1. Design Library

Product catalogs and samples (paint chips, stone veneer samples, brick veneer samples, tile samples, carpet samples, etc). You want to look at these samples **under natural light** to see how they will actually look after they are installed at the project site.

The Holistic Design Concept and Several Architecture, Planning, and Landscape Books to Help You Overcome "the Designer's Block"

I believe in a **holistic design approach**. To me, planning, architecture, and gardens are different aspects of the same overall design. They depend on each other and follow the same design principles. The following are several architecture, planning, and landscape books that I like to flip through to get some inspiration when I encounter "the designer's block":

a. *Architecture: Form, Space, & Order*
by Francis D. K. Ching

I read this book in Chinese when I started to learn architecture many years ago, and I bought the English version later when I came to the U.S. I love it. It is one of the best architectural books that you can have. I still flip through it every now and then. It is a great book to obtain inspiration.

b. *History of Urban Form: Before the Industrial Revolution*
by A. E. J. Morris

My professor introduced this book to us as the textbook for a core course when I was studying for my master's degree at the School of Architecture, University of Southern California in Los Angeles. I bought it for the class, and I loved it and kept it with me ever since. It has many great line drawings to illustrate city and urban planning and architecture in many different cultures throughout history. It enlightens you and encourages you to look at a design issue on a grand scale. With very powerful images, it will show you how brilliant human beings can be.

c. *The Landscape of Man: Shaping the Environment from Prehistory to the Present Day*
by Geoffrey Alan Jellicoe

What is "Landscape of Man"?

"To qualify as 'landscape of man,' an environment must be deliberately shaped at a specific time…Art is a continuous process …" Sir Geoffrey Jellicoe and his wife Susan wrote, "All design therefore derives from impressions of the past, conscious or subconscious, and in the modern collective landscape, from historic gardens and parks and silhouettes which were created for totally different social reasons …"

The Landscape of Man: Shaping the Environment from Prehistory to the Present Day includes 28 sections that are separated into two parts.

Part One is "From Prehistory to the end of the Seventeenth Century." It covers landscape from prehistory to 1700 AD and includes 17 sections covering Origins, Central Civilization (Western Asia to the Muslim Conquest, Islam in Western Asia, the Western Expansion of Islam: Spain, the Eastern Expansion of Islam: Mughul India), Eastern Civilization (Ancient India, China, Japan, Pre-Columbian America), and Western Civilization (Egypt, Greece, the Roman Empire, the Middle Ages in Europe, Italy: the Renaissance, France: sixteenth and seventeenth centuries, Spain, Germany, England, the Netherlands: sixteenth and seventeenth centuries). The text for each section follows a standard format of environment, social history, philosophy, expression, architecture, and landscape. Case studies have striking black-and-white photos, paintings, and plans, as well as a brief description.

Part Two of the book is "The Evolution of Modern Landscape." It covers landscape from 1700 AD to the present and includes 11 sections covering the eighteenth century (Western Classicism, the Chinese school, the English school), the nineteenth century (the European mainland, the British Isles, the United States of America), and the twentieth century (Europe, the Americas, the Western Hemisphere: the New World, the Eastern Hemisphere: the Old World), and the world's trends in landscape design. The text follows a standard format of environment, history, social influence, economics, philosophy, and expression for each century, and then a standard format of the home, landscape, comments, and case studies for each section.

The Landscape of Man: Shaping the Environment from Prehistory to the Present Day contains 408 pages, 746 illustrations, and 6 maps. It is a great book for architects, landscape architects, and urban planners!

d. *Great Gardens of the World: In Search of Paradise*
by Penelope Hobhouse

The following is a book review that I wrote:

Around the world in 240 pages!

Gardens are meant to be a paradise on earth. The idea of paradise as a garden has a long history, even before the Garden of Eden was presented in the Bible. There is hardly any specific description of what paradise looks like. The description of the Garden of Eden was not very specific either, yet, it gave the garden designer some ideas.

In every culture, garden designers seek paradise through their own creative ways. Penelope Hobhouse, one of the most talented garden writers of our time, starts her tour of paradise on earth in Asia: the serene naturalistic gardens and symbolism in China, and the Zen gardens and tea gardens in Japan. She then takes us to continental Europe: the hilly regions of Italy, where lavish gardens are balanced with the use of axes and symmetry, and gardens in Germany, the Netherlands, and Russia, as well as the climax of formal gardens, the French gardens.

Penelope Hobhouse's next stop was England. She discusses in detail the naturalistic landscape gardens, cottage-style gardens, and the eclectic gardens. She also explores Mediterranean gardens and gardens in America: European influences and   naturalistic   gardens.

Last, but not least, Penelope Hobhouse discusses today's gardens: water in gardens, gardens and nature, selecting the right plants for the right sites, reclaiming and revitalizing, and roof gardens, etc.

To Penelope, an ideal garden is "at the balance point between human control and untamed nature."

Great Gardens of the World: In Search of Paradise contains 240 pages and many beautiful interior color photos. It is an excellent garden book that every garden lover should have.

e. *Sunset Western Garden Book*
by Kathleen Norris Brenzel

Most of the existing books on landscaping can be put into one of these three categories:

1) Coffee table books with pretty photos
2) Encyclopedia of plants
3) Horticulture books

Only a few of the books on landscaping actually discuss design.

Sunset Western Garden Book is one of the best books for plant selection, a very important aspect of planting design. I have used it for many, many years. Every landscape architect that I know owns a copy of this book. Each new edition gets better and better.

Sunset Western Garden Book is one of the best encyclopedias and is the "bible" of Western gardening. As the author of *Planting Design Illustrated*, I would not hesitate to recommend this book to garden lovers.

This book is helpful to an architect because when you first start a design, you need to coordinate the landscape architect's design with your design. You can refer to this book and quickly determine the mature <u>size</u> of a tree and its <u>shape</u> and <u>density of its leaves</u> and know if it will block an important <u>view or signage</u>, etc.

This is the best plant encyclopedia for the Western United States. If you live in other areas, you can find a similar plant encyclopedia for your area to include in your library. These books are worthy owning.

2. General Library

There are many books in an architectural office, but **there are only a certain number of books that are used frequently.** I shall list them here and briefly discuss them. My advice to you is to at least look through the table of contents of these books, then flip through the pages, in order to **know where to locate the information** when you need it.

a. Codes, Acts and Regulations

American with Disabilities Act (ADA), *International Building Codes* (IBC), *Uniform Building Codes* (UBC) and their Local Adaptations, etc.

When you start to work on a project, the first thing that you need to do is **to call the city and find out which version of the codes the city is using.** For example, the *2007 California Building Code* (**CBC**) based on 2006 IBC, *2007 California Plumbing Code* (**CPC**) based on *2006 Uniform Plumbing Code* (**UPC**), *2007 California Mechanical Code* (**CPC**) based on *2006 Uniform Mechanical Code* (**UPC**), etc. This will save you a lot of time.

For example, before International Council of Building Officials (**ICBO**)/*Uniform Building Code*, Building Officials Conference of America (**BOCA**)/*BOCA Basic Building Code*, and Southern Building Code Congress International (**SBCCI**)/ *Southern Building Code* merged together as International Code Council (**ICC**) and consolidated all three codes as *International Building Code* (**IBC**), UBC was the basis of California Building Code.

The plumbing fixture requirement in UBC is different from the Plumbing Code. It makes a difference if the city is using UBC instead of the Plumbing Code for plumbing fixture counts. Some cities, like San Jose in California, have their own plumbing fixture requirements, which may require more plumbing fixtures than typical model codes.

The following are some of the commonly used books, regulations, codes, and acts:

1) **American with Disabilities Act (ADA)**

On July 26, 1990, President George H. W. Bush signed into law the Americans with Disabilities Act of 1990 (ADA)—the world's first comprehensive civil rights law for people with disabilities. The Act prohibits discrimination against people with disabilities in employment (Title I), in public services (Title II), in public accommodations (Title III), and in telecommunications (Title IV). ADA has significant impact on architectural design.

All public buildings are required to accommodate people with disabilities. This means public buildings need to have **handicap ramps** at main entrances, handicap **paths of travel** from the main building entrance to public sidewalks, a minimum number of **handicap parking stalls** close to building entrances, a minimum height for electrical outlets, and a maximum height of operational parts for the telephone, maximum height for counters, **knee spaces** under the counter, etc.

The full text of **"ADA Standards for Accessible Design"** and related illustrations/diagrams are available at:

http://www.ada.gov/stdspdf.htm

2) *Title 24, California Disabled Accessibility Guidebook* (**CalDAG**) *& California Accessibility Reference Manual Code & Checklist* (**CARM**)

For California, Title 24 has a set of accessibility regulations, which are not exactly the same as the Federal ADA provisions.

Both books (CalDAG & CARM) blend California's accessibility regulations with Federal ADA provisions and sort out and explain the differences between the ADA & Title 24 that all California professionals must understand and apply to comply with both laws. **CalDAG** has 14 flow charts, 250 computer-generated details, and complete checklists. **CARM** has more than 50 tables, 800 unique line drawings, and cross-referencing to the ADA and California's Title 24.

If you purchase one or both of the books, they can save much wasted time and effort. The money will be well spent.

The latest versions of these books may <u>not</u> be available at Amazon, but they are available at:

http://www.buildersbooksource.com/

Although these accessibility codes and regulations seem complicated, there are <u>only a few important items</u> that you need to memorize:

a) You need to know the **Paths of Travel (POT)** for handicap people; i.e., from an accessible entrance or an emergency exit, you need to maintain a continuous **Path of Travel** to the <u>public</u> sidewalks. Along the path, you can only have a maximum of <u>2%</u> cross slope. If a slope along the direction of travel is over <u>5%</u>, it becomes a ramp and may require railing per codes.

   If a <u>curb</u> ramp slope is between <u>5%</u> and <u>6.67%</u>, then you definitely need to provide truncated domes.

   Note: Truncated domes are warning finishes for handicap slopes or borders to traffic area. They are expensive to build, even the prefabricated ones, costing thousands of dollars.

   If a <u>curb</u> ramp slope is between <u>6.67% and 8.33%</u> (<u>maximum slope allowed for a ramp</u>), then you may <u>NOT</u> need to provide truncated domes if your project is outside of California. Therefore, you want to make the slope <u>either less than 5 percent% or between 6.67% and 8.33%</u>. See the two books mentioned above for details.

b) The handrails for ramps and stairs are <u>2'-10"</u> high minimum, while a typical guardrail height is <u>3'-6"</u> minimum. The handrails for a ramp need to have a <u>12" extension</u> at the top and bottom of the ramp, while the handrails for stairs need to have a <u>12"</u> extension at the top of the stairs and <u>12" PLUS the depth of one thread at the bottom</u> of the stairs. You need to know the maximum height of a stair riser is <u>7"</u>, and the minimum depth of a stair thread is <u>11"</u> (**Mnemonics**: <u>7/11</u>).

   You need to know how to detail the <u>transition</u> between the handrails and guardrails. Some designers just run the handrails and their extension behind the guardrails and anchor them to the guardrail support. You can learn a lot by paying attention to these kinds of details when you look at a building.

c) You can simply look through the two books mentioned above and become familiar with the handicap diagrams and the main dimension clearances required, such as <u>5'-0"</u> wheelchair **turning radius**, <u>1'-6"</u> <u>clearance</u> from the centerline of the sinks and toilet to the walls, 2'-10" maximum handicap counter height, knee spaces below the sinks and workstations, clearance space in front of the sinks and workstations, maximum and minimum heights of operating parts of a telephone, minimum corridor widths, etc. These dimensions are very important, especially for handicap toilets, workstations, etc. At least you need to know where to find the information and dimension diagrams when you need them.

On a separate note: **in California, another main item that an architect needs to coordinate is the T-24 Calcs.** You as the architect need to review and sign the building envelop form both in the T-24 calcs books and on the T-24 calcs drawing sheet (typically as part of the mechanical drawing set). You also need to coordinate with your mechanical engineer and/or the T-24 calcs consultant to make sure that you specify the proper glazing (**¼" thick** glazing **or 1" insulated** glazing, i.e., two layers of ¼" glazing with a ½" air space between them) for windows, insulation for ceiling and walls per T-24 calcs.

Please also pay attention to the **thickness of the insulation.**

For example, if you have R-30 Batt insulation under your roof, your insulation is about **10" thick**, and if you have 2 x 6 wood roof sub-purlins, you will have a problem in installing the R-30 Batt insulation since you cannot press the insulation to fit in the 5½" deep space between the roof sub-purlins.

Note: 2 x 6 are the nominal dimensions for wood studs; the actual dimensions for them are 1½" x 5½". This is typical for wood studs, i.e., the actual dimensions for 2 x 4 wood studs are 1 ½" x 3 ½," etc.

You will have to coordinate with your consultant to find out if he can use R-19 instead of R-30, or you may need to use rigid insulation over the roof sheathing instead of Batt insulation under the roof deck. Similarly, make sure your furred walls or stud walls can accommodate the thickness of your wall insulation (both Batt and rigid insulation).

3) *International Building Code* (IBC) and Its Local Adaptations

This is compiled by the **International Code Council (ICC)** and published by Delmar Cengage Learning. A new edition comes out every 3 years. It is the model code adapted by 48 states in the U.S. as the building code. Most state codes will be updated 1 year after the new edition of IBC comes out.

This book is very important, and it applies to all phases of architectural design. For example, at the very beginning of the project, you may need to refer to this code for **building qualifications**, for **allowable areas and allowable area increases** to find out how big a building you can build, **which construction type** you can choose, **how many plumbing fixtures** (toilets, urinals, sinks, etc.) that you need to provide for each sex, etc.

When you are developing the construction documents for city submittals, you may need to refer to this code for the **minimum number of exits and exit width** required, the **minimum distance required between at least two exits** (typically it is not less than ½ of the diagonal distance of the space in which these two exits are located), the maximum travel distance to an exit, etc. This book is not only useful for architects, but also very useful for structural engineers.

4) Other International Code Council (ICC) Codes

ICC also compiles and publishes several other codes. You need to know about them but may not need to buy them, since you should be able to depend on your consultants for their knowledge and expertise in their fields. (If you cannot count on them, you may need to find better consultants.)

These codes include:

ICC Electrical Code Administrative Provisions
International Mechanical Code
International Plumbing Code
International Fuel & Gas Code
International Fire Code
International Energy Conservation Code

There are a few other special codes by the ICC:

International Property Maintenance Code
International Residential Code
International Existing Building Code

For the latest version of International Codes, check **International Code Council's** website at:

http://www.iccsafe.org/

5) *National Electrical Code* **(NEC)**

Electrical Code is a little different from other codes. Many states adapt the *National Electrical Code* instead of a code by the ICC.

6) Municipal Codes

Many cities have their own municipal codes, which include sections on planning, building, etc. Therefore, you also need to check a city's website or call the local city office to find out if they have their own municipal codes.

7) *Building Codes Illustrated: A Guide to Understanding the 2006 International Building Code*

This book is written by Francis Ching & Steven R. Winkel. It is a valuable interpretive guide with many useful line drawings and is a great timesaver.

b. **Reference Books:** *The Steel Book,* LEED Reference Guides and Documents, etc.

The Steel Book

The full name of this book is actually *Steel Construction Manual.* It is published by the American Institute of Steel Construction. This is a very expensive but also very valuable book for both architects and structural engineers. Architects find it useful to look up the sectional dimensions for columns and beams, and also their structural weight per linear foot, and then they can **find out if their columns will fit inside an interior partition** or find out the height of the beams, and then subtract the floor thickness, **beam height,** mechanical duct height, and ceiling thickness to **calculate the actual ceiling heights** for spaces under a mezzanine, etc.

LEED Reference Guides and Documents

These reference guides and documents are published by the U.S. Green Building Council (USGBC). There are a few reference guides and documents regarding the USGBC Green Building Rating system:

LEED New Construction (LEED NC)
LEED Existing Buildings (LEED EB)
LEED Core and Shell (LEED CS)
LEED Commercial Interior (LEED CI)
LEED for Schools

In 2009, some new versions of reference guides become available:

The LEED 2009 Reference Guide for Green Building Design and Construction
(Based on and incorporated guidance for the three LEED rating systems: LEED 2009 for New Construction and Major Renovations, LEED 2009 for Schools New Construction and Major Renovations, and LEED 2009 for Core & Shell Development.)

The LEED 2009 Reference Guide for Green Building Operations and Maintenance
(Based on and incorporated guidance for LEED 2009 for Existing Buildings: Operations & Maintenance Rating System.)

The LEED 2009 Reference Guide for Green Interior Design and Construction

(Based on and incorporated guidance for the LEED 2009 for Commercial Interiors Green Building Rating System.)

See the links below for the latest versions of the LEED reference guides and documents:
http://www.usgbc.org/Store/PublicationsList.aspx?CMSPageID=1518
http://www.usgbc.org/DisplayPage.aspx?CMSPageID=1762

See the link below for LEED Resources:

http://www.usgbc.org/DisplayPage.aspx?CMSPageID=75

Architectural Graphic Standards

For over 70 years, architects have been using a valuable reference book called *Architectural Graphic Standards*. I like the Tenth Edition better than the Eleventh Edition.

Architectural Graphic Standards is organized roughly per the CSI MasterFormat divisions, including general planning and design data, site work, concrete, masonry, metals, wood, thermal and moisture protection, doors and windows, finishes, specialties, equipment, furnishings, special construction, conveying systems, mechanical, electrical, sports, energy, history preservation, etc.

Architectural Graphic Standards is in 9.6 x 11.8 inch large format and has numerous line drawings. This edition has expanded and added new content covering contemporary issues. It is a must-have for architects, landscape architects, urban planners, interior designers, engineers, or any other building-related design professionals.

Most of the time, I use it to look up some important dimensions for technical data or to refresh my memory or to clarify some issues.

Building Construction Illustrated
by Francis Ching

The illustrations are great! Ching has a wonderful talent to simplify complicated issues and make them very easy to understand. This is a great book to learn wood stud construction.

c. AIA and Commonly Used AIA Forms

You can buy hard copies of AIA forms or AIA form software from www.AIA.org or your local AIA office. For contract documents, **do NOT copy AIA forms and placed them in your spec. books,** because these forms are protected by copyright laws. You can simply note the name of the AIA form and the version to be used in the spec. books, then have the contractors obtain the forms from local AIA offices or by calling 800-365-2724 or contact AIA national headquarters at

http://www.aia.org/

The AIA forms include the following series:

A-Series: owner-contract documents, mainly for contracts between the owner and the contractor or furniture, furnishings, and equipment (FF&E) vendor, or owner's instructions to them.

B-Series: owner-architect agreements

C-Series: architect-consultant documents

D-Series: architect-industry documents

E-Series: digital practice documents

G-Series: architect's office and project forms

You can download some **free** AIA documents at:

http://www.aia.org/docs_free_paperdocuments

These **free** documents include some very valuable forms and information, such as:

Comparison, A201™-97 to A201™-07

A201™-2007 Commentary, Commentary on AIA Document A201™-2007

Comparison, B101™-2007 to B151™-1997

The following is a list of **commonly used AIA forms:**

A101™-2007, Standard Form of Agreement between Owner and Contractor Where the Basis of Payment Is a Stipulated Sum

A201™-2007, General Conditions of the Contract for Construction

B141™-1997 Part 1/Part 2, Standard Form of Agreement between Owner and Architect with Standard Form of Architect's Services

B151™-1997, Abbreviated Standard Form of Agreement between Owner and Architect

C141™-1997, Standard Form of Agreement between Architect and Consultant

C142™-1997, Abbreviated Standard Form of Agreement between Architect and Consultant

D101™-1995, Architectural Building Area and Volume Measurement

D200™-1995, Project Checklist

G701™-2001, Change Order

G702™-1992, Application and Certificate for Payment

G703™-1992, Continuation Sheet (for G702™-1992)

G704™-2000, Certificate of Substantial Completion

G712™-1972, Shop Drawing and Sample Record

G714™-2007, Construction Change Directive

G716™-2004, Request for Information

You need to become acquainted with these AIA forms and **buy at least one copy of the commonly used forms and read them word-for-word at least once** so that you know what information is contained on these forms and know where to find the information when you need it.

The following is a link for **a complete list of the latest version of AIA forms and their prices:**

http://www.aia.org/SiteObjects/files/docs_paperpricelist.pdf

d. CSI MasterFormat, *Sweets Catalog*, and Various Manufacturers' Product Catalogs

Sweets Catalog is a catalog of MANY different manufacturers' information. It arranges the manufacturers' information per the **CSI MasterFormat's divisions.** It is published by McGraw-Hill Construction, and has over 1,500 products and manufacturers' CAD details, including dwg and pdf format files. See the link below for the latest version:

http://products.construction.com/

The CSI MasterFormat is the organizational standard for specifications developed by **Construction Specifications Institute (CSI)** and **Construction Specifications Canada (CSC).** It is very important and widely used in North America, especially for the commercial and institutional building projects. The current version is MasterFormat 2004 (MF04) Edition. It replaces MasterFormat 1995 (MF95), and **expands the well-known "16 Divisions" (Divisions 1 to 16) to 50 Divisions (Divisions 0 to 49)** of construction information.

You need to know both the new and the old versions of MasterFormat because many projects and manufacturers are still using the old version, and the new version does not completely change the old version except for divisions 15 and 16. All other new divisions are simply added to the older version.

The new version uses six digits instead of five digits: the first two digits are the division number, or **level one**; the next two digits are **level two**; the third set of two digits are **level three**. Sometimes, another set of two-digit numbers are added after a dot. This fourth set of digits are **level four**. The **level four** numbers are NOT defined by MasterFormat, and they are used only when necessary.

For example, for "03 52 16. 13 Lightweight Cellular Insulating Concrete," the first two digits, "03," are the division number, or level one; the next two digits, "52," are level two; the third set of two digits, "16," are level three; the fourth set of two digits, number "13," are added after a dot.

For most of the old five-digit division numbers, you can simply add a zero to the end and convert them to the new six-digit division numbers. For example, the old division "01100 Summary" will become new division "01 10 00 Summary."

See the link below for more information on **converting your old MF95 numbers to MF04 numbers:**

http://www.masterformat.com/transitionguide/

Both the "old" and new CSI MasterFormat divisions are listed below, and the **new divisions are shown in bold fonts:**

Table 1.2   Comparing Old and New Versions of MasterFormat

Procuring and Contracting Requirements Group:

Division 00 00 00   **Procuring and Contracting Requirements**
Introductory Information
Bidding Requirements
Contracting Requirements
Facilities and Spaces
Systems and Assemblies

Specifications Group:

General Requirements Subgroup:

Division 1　　　　　　　General Requirements **(New Version Division Number: 01 00 00)**

　　　　01100　　Summary

　　　　01200　　Price and Payment Procedures

　　　　01300　　Administrative Requirements

　　　　01400　　Quality Requirements

　　　　01500　　Temporary Facilities and Controls

　　　　01600　　Product Requirements

　　　　01700　　Execution Requirements

　　　　01800　　Facility Operation

　　　　01900　　Facility Decommissioning

Facility Construction Subgroup:

Division 2　　　　　　　Site Construction **(New Version: Division 02 00 00 Existing Condition)**

　　　　02050　　Basic Site Materials and Methods

　　　　02100　　Site Remediation

　　　　02200　　Site Preparation

　　　　02300　　Earthwork

　　　　02400　　Tunneling, Boring, and Jacking

　　　　02450　　Foundation and Load-Bearing Elements

　　　　02500　　Utility Services

　　　　02600　　Drainage and Containment

　　　　02700　　Bases, Ballasts, Pavements, and Appurtenances

　　　　02800　　Site Improvements and Amenities

　　　　02900　　Planting

　　　　02950　　Site Restoration and Rehabilitation

Division 3　　　　　　　Concrete **(New Version Division Number: 03 00 00)**

　　　　03050　　Basic Concrete Materials and Methods

　　　　03100　　Concrete Forms and Accessories

　　　　03200　　Concrete Reinforcement

　　　　03300　　Cast-In-Place Concrete

　　　　03400　　Precast Concrete

　　　　03500　　Cementitious Decks and Underlayment

　　　　03600　　Grouts

　　　　03700　　Mass Concrete

　　　　03900　　Concrete Restoration and Cleaning

Division 4　　　　　　　Masonry **(New Version Division Number: 04 00 00)**

　　　　04050　　Basic Masonry Materials and Methods

　　　　04200　　Masonry Units

	04400	Stone
	04500	Refractories
	04600	Corrosion-Resistant Masonry
	04700	Simulated Masonry
	04800	Masonry Assemblies
	04900	Masonry Restoration and Cleaning

Division 5		Metals **(New Version Division Number: 05 00 00)**
	05050	Basic Metal Materials and Methods
	05100	Structural Metal Framing
	05200	Metal Joists
	05300	Metal Deck
	05400	Cold-Formed Metal Framing
	05500	Metal Fabrications
	05600	Hydraulic Fabrications
	05700	Ornamental Metal
	05800	Expansion Control
	05900	Metal Restoration and Cleaning

Division 6		Wood and Plastics **(New Version: Division 06 00 00 Wood, Plastics, and Composites)**
	06050	Basic Wood and Plastic Materials and Methods
	06100	Rough Carpentry
	06200	Finish Carpentry
	06400	Architectural Woodwork
	06500	Structural Plastics
	06600	Plastic Fabrications
	06900	Wood and Plastic Restoration and Cleaning

Division 7		Thermal and Moisture Protection **(New Version Division Number: 07 00 00)**
	07050	Basic Thermal and Moisture Protection Materials and Methods
	07100	Damproofing and Waterproofing
	07200	Thermal Protection
	07300	Shingles, Roof Tiles, and Roof Coverings
	07400	Roofing and Siding Panels
	07500	Membrane Roofing
	07600	Flashing and Sheet Metal
	07700	Roof Specialties and Accessories
	07800	Fire and Smoke Protection
	07900	Joint Sealers

Division 8		Doors and Windows **(New Version: Division 08 00 00 Openings)**
	08050	Basic Door and Window Materials and Methods
	08100	Metal Doors and Frames

08200	Wood and Plastic Doors
08300	Specialty Doors
08400	Entrances and Storefronts
08500	Windows
08600	Skylights
08700	Hardware
08800	Glazing
08900	Glazed Curtain Wall

Division 9		Finishes **(New Version Division Number: 09 00 00)**
	09050	Basic Finish Materials and Methods
	09100	Metal Support Assemblies
	09200	Plaster and Gypsum Board
	09300	Tile
	09400	Terrazzo
	09500	Ceilings
	09600	Flooring
	09700	Wall Finishes
	09800	Acoustical Treatment
	09900	Paints and Coatings

Division 10		Specialties **(New Version Division Number: 10 00 00)**
	10100	Visual Display Boards
	10150	Compartments and Cubicles
	10200	Louvers and Vents
	10240	Grilles and Screens
	10250	Service Walls
	10260	Wall and Corner Guards
	10270	Access Flooring
	10290	Pest Control
	10300	Fireplaces and Stoves
	10340	Manufactured Exterior Specialties
	10350	Flagpoles
	10400	Identification Devices
	10450	Pedestrian Control Devices
	10500	Lockers
	10520	Fire Protection Specialties
	10530	Protective Covers
	10550	Postal Specialties
	10600	Partitions
	10670	Storage Shelving
	10700	Exterior Protection
	10750	Telephone Specialties
	10800	Toilet, Bath, and Laundry Specialties

10880	Scales
10900	Wardrobe and Closet Specialties

Division 11   Equipment **(New Version Division Number: 11 00 00)**

11010	Maintenance Equipment
11020	Security and Vault Equipment
11030	Teller and Service Equipment
11040	Ecclesiastical Equipment
11050	Library
11060	Theater and Stage Equipment
11070	Instrumental Equipment
11080	Registration Equipment
11090	Checkroom Equipment
11100	Mercantile Equipment
11110	Commercial Laundry and Dry Cleaning Equipment
11120	Vending Equipment
11130	Audio-Visual Equipment
11140	Vehicle Service Equipment
11150	Parking Control Equipment
11160	Loading Dock Equipment
11170	Solid Waste Handling Equipment
11190	Detention Equipment
11200	Water Supply and Treatment Equipment
11280	Hydraulic Gates and Valves
11300	Fluid Waste Treatment and Disposal Equipment
11400	Food Service Equipment
11450	Residential Equipment
11460	Unit Kitchens
11470	Darkroom Equipment
11480	Athletic, Recreational, and Therapeutic Equipment
11500	Industrial and Process Equipment
11600	Laboratory Equipment
11650	Planetarium Equipment
11660	Observatory Equipment
11680	Office Equipment
11700	Medical Equipment
11780	Mortuary Equipment
11850	Navigation Equipment
11870	Agricultural Equipment
11900	Exhibit Equipment

Division 12   Furnishings **(New Version Division Number: 12 00 00)**

12050	Fabrics
12100	Art

	12300	Manufactured Casework
	12400	Furnishings and Accessories
	12500	Furniture
	12600	Multiple Seating
	12700	Systems Furniture
	12800	Interior Plants and Planters
	12900	Furnishings Restoration and Repair
Division 13		Special Construction (New Version Division Number: 13 00 00)
	13010	Air-Supported Structures
	13020	Building Modules
	13030	Special Purpose Rooms
	13080	Sound, Vibration, and Seismic Control
	13090	Radiation Protection
	13100	Lightning Protection
	13110	Cathodic Protection
	13120	Pre-Engineered Structures
	13150	Swimming Pools
	13160	Aquariums
	13165	Aquatic Park Facilities
	13170	Tubs and Pools
	13175	Ice Rinks
	13185	Kennels and Animal Shelters
	13190	Site-Constructed Incinerators
	13200	Storage Tanks
	13220	Filter Underdrains and Media
	13230	Digester Covers and Appurtenances
	13240	Oxygenation Systems
	13260	Sludge Conditioning Systems
	13280	Hazardous Material Remediation
	13400	Measurement and Control Instrumentation
	13500	Recording Instrumentation
	13550	Transportation Control Instrumentation
	13600	Solar and Wind Energy Equipment
	13700	Security Access and Surveillance
	13800	Building Automation and Control
	13850	Detection and Alarm
	13900	Fire Suppression
Division 14		Conveying Systems (New Version: Division 14 00 00 Conveying Equipment)
	14100	Dumbwaiters
	14200	Elevators
	14300	Escalators and Moving Walks
	14400	Lifts

	14500	Material Handling
	14600	Hoists and Cables
	14700	Turntables
	14800	Scaffolding
	14900	Transportation

Division 15 — Mechanical **(In New Version: Division 15 is changed to "Reserved for Future Expansion," and Mechanical is spread as parts of Divisions 21 00 00, 22 00 00, and 23 00 00, etc., of the new version)**

	15050	Basic Mechanical Materials and Methods
	15100	Building Service Piping
	15200	Process Piping
	15300	Fire Protection Piping
	15400	Plumbing Fixtures and Equipment
	15500	Heat-Generation Equipment
	15600	Refrigeration Equipment
	15700	Heating, Ventilating, and Air-Conditioning Equipment
	15800	Air Distribution
	15900	HVAC Instrumentation and Controls
	15950	Testing, Adjusting, and Balancing

Division 16 — Electrical **(In New Version: Division 16 is changed to "Reserved for Future Expansion," and Electrical is spread as parts of Divisions 26 00 00, 27 00 00, and 28 00 00, etc., of the new version)**

	16050	Basic Electrical Materials and Methods
	16100	Wiring Methods
	16200	Electrical Power
	16300	Transmission and Distribution
	16400	Low-Voltage Distribution
	16500	Lighting
	16700	Communications
	16800	Sound and Video

New Version of MasterFormat also includes the following new divisions:

Division 17 00 00   **Reserved for Future Expansion**

Division 18 00 00   **Reserved for Future Expansion**

Facility Services Subgroup:

Division 20 00 00   **Reserved for Future Expansion**

Division 21 00 00   **Fire Suppression**

Division 22 00 00	**Plumbing**
Division 23 00 00	**Heating, Ventilation, and Air Conditioning**
Division 24 00 00	**Reserved for Future Expansion**
Division 25 00 00	**Integrated Automation**
Division 26 00 00	**Electrical**
Division 27 00 00	**Communications**
Division 28 00 00	**Electronic Safety and Security**
Division 29 00 00	**Reserved for Future Expansion**

Site and Infrastructure Subgroup:

Division 30 00 00	**Reserved for Future Expansion**
Division 31 00 00	**Earthwork**
Division 32 00 00	**Exterior Improvements**
Division 33 00 00	**Utilities**
Division 34 00 00	**Transportation**
Division 35 00 00	**Waterway and Marine**
Division 36 00 00	**Reserved for Future Expansion**
Division 37 00 00	**Reserved for Future Expansion**
Division 38 00 00	**Reserved for Future Expansion**
Division 39 00 00	**Reserved for Future Expansion**

Process Equipment Subgroup:

Division 40 00 00	**Process Integration**
Division 41 00 00	**Material Processing and Handling Equipment**
Division 42 00 00	**Process Heating, Cooling, and Drying Equipment**
Division 43 00 00	**Process Gas and Liquid Handling, Purification and Storage Equipment**
Division 44 00 00	**Pollution Control Equipment**
Division 45 00 00	**Industry-Specific Manufacturing Equipment**
Division 46 00 00	**Reserved for Future Expansion**

Division 47 00 00   **Reserved for Future Expansion**

Division 48 00 00   **Electrical Power Generation**

Division 49 00 00   **Reserved for Future Expansion**

For all **new** projects, you should **use the new MasterFormat numbers whenever possible.**

You need to at least memorize the major MasterFormat divisions. For example, if people mention Division 3, you should know it is concrete, and vice versa.

See the links below for the latest version of MasterFormat, **new MasterFormat numbers**, and a **free conversion tool/link of the old MasterFormat numbers to the new MasterFormat CSI number:**

http://www.csinet.org/s_csi/sec.asp?TRACKID=&CID=1377&DID=11339

http://www.masterformat.com/

You can also register and download the MasterFormat White Paper at:
http://www.csinet.org/s_csi/sec.asp?Trackid=&CID=756&DID=14845

In addition to *Sweets Catalog*, each manufacturer often has its own catalogs, and most of the architectural offices arrange these catalogs on the bookshelf of the office library per the **CSI MasterFormat divisions.**

e. Computer-Aided Design & Drafting & other CADD Books

The following is a list of commonly used CADD software often found in an architectural office:

AutoCAD (the dominant software for the construction industry)

ArchiCAD (a 3-D drafting software with good 2-D functions; commonly used in Europe, but not in the U.S.)

MicroStation (two main retailers in the U.S., Albertsons and Target, use it. Some government agencies also use it.)

Photoshop (commonly used for rendering commercial bitmap and image manipulation)

Sketch-Up (a 3-D sketching software for the conceptual phases of design; commonly used for building 3-D models or animation)

You can easily do a quick search on Amazon and find many good CADD books. I highly recommend one particular book called *Mastering AutoCAD*, by George Omura. George has been writing and updating this book for many years. It is filled with many useful tips and tricks, and it is **tailored for architecture.**

The commonly used layer standard is the AIA CAD standards or AIA CAD Layer Guidelines. See the link below for more information:

http://www.cad-design-and-drafting-services.com/aia-cad-standards.html

3. **Commonly Used Manufacturers' & Various Websites**

In addition to the websites mentioned earlier in this book, many manufacturers have very detailed websites. They provide information that can be used by both designers and the production team.

Sweets Catalog arranges the manufacturers and their websites per the MasterFormat divisions. Some offices also arrange these websites per the MasterFormat divisions. You can compile a complete list for your office or simply subscribe to *Sweets Catalog* and use the websites that they compile.

I am NOT going to list all these websites here and compile a complete list because each region may have different manufacturers available. I shall only discuss or list some well-known and commonly used manufacturers and their websites, and I shall use the latest MasterFormat number to arrange them. You can get the latest information from these sites:

04 00 00   Masonry

There are two main categories of bricks: **full bricks** and **thin bricks.** Thin bricks are much easier to install, but full bricks look better. There are specific requirements regarding full bricks per building codes. For example, over an opening, full bricks support has to be able to transfer the load to the ground instead of the cantilever. In some cases, you may have no choice but to use thin bricks.

Some useful links:

Masonry Institute of America
http://www.masonryinstitute.org/

Pacific Clay Products, Inc.
http://www.pacificclay.com/

04 73 00   Manufactured Stone Masonry

Per building codes, if the stone veneer weighs over 2 lbs per s.f., you need to design anchors, etc., to support it. If the stone veneer weighs less than 2 lbs per s.f., then you can simply set it in mortar. This is a much easier installation method. See each manufacturer's website for specific recommendations for installation. Some useful links:

Coronado Stone (natural-looking artificial stones; they are much cheaper than real stones and look like real stones)
http://www.coronado.com/

Eldorado Stone (natural-looking artificial stones; they are much cheaper than real stones, and look like real stones)
http://www.eldoradostone.com/

Cultured Stone (natural-looking artificial stones; they are much cheaper than real stones, and look like real stones)

http://www.culturedstone.com/

06 09 00   Wood and Plastic Fastenings

Simpson StrongTie
http://www.strongtie.com/

I use this website to look up the structural connectors for wood structures, like trellises, etc. You can pick a connector that looks good by just looking through the catalog at this website. Believe me, **you do not want to have your structural engineer select exposed connectors.** They know structural issues, but they do not know aesthetics as well as you, the architect.

07 00 00   Thermal and Moisture Protection

07 20 00   Thermal Protection

There are two main categories of insulation: **Batt insulation and rigid insulation.** Batt insulation sometimes has foil or other kinds of backing. It is installed UNDER the roof structure or within the walls. Rigid insulation is installed OVER the roof sheathing or within the walls. It is also installed under the concrete slab in a cold climate or within the concrete slab under the freezer of supermarkets.

Johns Manville, a Berkshire Hathaway company, is a manufacturer and marketer of building insulation, commercial roofing, roof insulation, and specialty products.
http://www.jm.com/

07 32 00   Roof Tiles

There are two main categories of roof tiles: **concrete roof tile and clay roof tile.** Following the current trend of going green, many manufacturers have started to manufacture <u>light color, highly reflective</u> roof tiles. Some useful links:

Eagle Roofing is a main manufacturer of concrete roof tiles.
http://www.eagleroofing.com/

MonierLifetile (MLT) is a main manufacturer of both concrete roof tiles and clay roof tiles.
http://www.monierlifetile.com/

MCA Superior Clay Roof Tile
http://www.mca-tile.com/

07 50 00   **Membrane Roofing**

Roofing is very, very important for construction. Many people say that if you want to summarize a thick architectural specifications book in one sentence, it is **"Do NOT fall, and do NOT leak."** There is some truth to this. One of the main design intents of the entire set of construction documents (drawings and specifications book) is to keep water and moisture out of the building. That is why we have moisture barriers inside the walls and under the concrete slab. That is why we use roofing and flashing, etc.

Many major developers and tenants often hire an **independent roofing consultant** to do roof inspections before, during, and after the installation. All major construction projects also have **pre-roof meetings**.

There are two main categories of membrane roofing:

Bituminous Systems

They include **Built-Up Roofing** (two-ply roofing, three-ply roofing, four-ply roofing, and so on), **APP Modified Bitumen**, and **SBS Modified Bitumen** systems. Built-up roofing can be **hot applied** or **cold applied**. See each manufacturer's catalog and website for specific installation recommendations.

Single-Ply Roofing Systems

Single-ply roofing systems can be subdivided into **PVC, TPO,** and **EPDM** roofing systems. Single-ply roofing can be **mechanically fastened** or **fully adhered**. **EPDM** roofing can also be **ballasted**. Again, see each manufacturer's catalog and website for specific installation recommendations.

Built-up roofing has a long history, but more and more manufacturers are moving toward single-ply roofing.

You can run single-ply roofing all the way up along the back of the parapet walls and then over the top of the parapet and then connect to the drip edge at the front at the top of the parapet. This is extremely useful when you have a 15' to 20' **high parapet** (many retail buildings do have parapet at such heights).

I have actually used single-ply PVC roofing to cover the back of a retail building parapet that was over 20' high. This is also extremely useful when you have a wide (like 6' wide) and relatively flat parapet: you cannot cover it with **sheet metal** because it is too wide; you cannot cover it with a **standing seam metal roof** because it is too flat. Single-ply roofing is ideal to cover this type of **wide and relatively flat parapet,** and may be the only way to do it.

Many roofing manufacturers have a list of approved contractors to install their products.

Following the current trend of going green, many manufacturers have started to manufacture light color, highly reflective roofing.

The followings are some manufacturers for roofing products:

Johns Manville products
http://www.jm.com/

Firestone Building Products
http://www.firestonebpco.com/

GAF Materials Corporation
http://www.gaf.com/

08 41 00   **Entrances and Storefronts**

There are three kinds of common finishes for storefront systems: clear anodized, light bronze anodized, and dark bronze anodized finish. Please note that you **cannot paint** over the storefront **in the field** to change the color or texture of the finish because they are **powder coated.** Therefore, when you select the color of the storefront frame, you need to consider it in advance in relation to the colors of the adjacent surfaces.

The typical storefront frame size is **1¾" x 4"** or **1¾" x 6."**

The infill glass can be **¼" thick** glazing **or 1" insulated** glazing (two layers of ¼" glazing with a ½" air space between them).

The following are some commonly used manufacturers:

Kawneer Products
http://www.kawneer.com/

U.S. Aluminum Commercial Products Group
http://www.usalum.com/

Arcadia, Inc.
http://www.arcadiaincorporated.com/

09 30 00 **Tiling**

Ceramic tiles are one of the commonly used tiles. They are easy to clean, and they are one of the favorite choices for floor and wall finish for many health departments. You may want to use slip-resistant (but still easy to clean) tiles in areas where people will walk.

Following are some ceramic tile manufacturers and associations:

Dal-Tile Corporation
http://www.daltile.com/

National Tile Contractors Associations
http://www.ceramic-tile.com/

09 77 00 **Special Wall Surfacing**

FRP (fiberglass-reinforced panel) gives you new choices in decorative, sanitary wall surfaces.

FRP is easy to clean, and it is one of the favorite choices for wall finishes for health departments. Many health departments will required either a 4'-0" high or an 8'-0" high smooth and cleanable wall finish in bathrooms and janitors' rooms or rooms for food processing in retail buildings.

FRP or ceramic tiles are two very common wall surfaces to satisfy this requirement. Of course, you need to contact the proper county health department for your project to find out the specific requirements.

FRP manufacturer(s):

Marlite
http://www.marlite.com/

Several good sites for **specifications and various manufacturers and trade associations:**

Sweets Network
http://products.construction.com/

Portland Cement Association (a good site to check out cement plaster color and finish)
http://www.cement.org/stucco/

http://www.4specs.com/

http://www.arcat.com/

Fry Reglet Architectural Metals
(roof flashing, reveals and moldings, column covers, reveals and moldings, interior surface systems, acoustical wall panels, glazing systems, and specialty products, etc.)

http://www.fryreglet.com/

E. Project Filing System

To work efficiently, an architectural office needs to have a good filing system to easily file and retrieve information.

Almost all architectural projects have administration files, construction drawings and specifications, and submittals and samples. We can store drawings in flat files and storage tubes, and administration files and specifications in job boxes. We suggest the following filing system. It can be used for both computer filing and hard copy filing.

Each project should have the following folders:

Admin (for administration)

Design

DD (for design development)

CD (for construction documents)

The **admin** folder can be subdivided into the following folders (you can also create physical folders for projects with the same system and keep the files in your filing cabinet):

101 General Project (Information)

You can file preliminary design sketches, design site plans and elevations, site topography maps, site title reports, entitlement packages, etc., in this folder.

102 Contracts and Additional Service

You can file Contracts and Additional Service Requests and all the related paperwork, sketches, e-mail correspondence, etc., in this folder.

103 Owner Correspondence

You can file owner correspondence (letters, e-mails, phone call notes, and meeting minutes) in this folder.

104 Tenant Correspondence

You can file tenant correspondence (letters, e-mails, phone call notes, and meeting minutes) in this folder.

105 Public Agencies

You can file public agencies' correspondence (plan check applications, plan submittal forms and receipts, school fee applications and receipts, plan check correction lists, letters, e-mails, phone call notes, and meeting minutes) in this folder.

106 Bidding

You can file bidding correspondence (invitations to bid, instructions to bidders, bid forms, related letters, e-mails, phone call notes, and pre-bid meeting minutes) in this folder.

107 Revisions—Addenda and Bulletins

You can file revisions (addenda and bulletins) and related letters, e-mails, phone call notes, and meeting minutes in this folder.

108 Contractors—RFI

You can file contractor's correspondence (RFI and related responses, letters, e-mails, phone call notes, and meeting minutes) in this folder.

109 Pay App and Change Order

You can file contractors' payment applications (Pay App) and conditional and unconditional waivers, change order requests, and related responses, letters, e-mails, phone notes, and meeting minutes in this folder.

110 Field Reports and Meeting Minutes

You can file field reports and meeting minutes and related letters, photos, e-mails, and phone call notes in this folder.

111 Consultants

You can file consultants' correspondence (letters, e-mails, phone call notes, and meeting minutes) in this folder. If the project is large, you can subdivide this folder to structural, electrical, mechanical, and plumbing engineers' folders, etc.

112 Calculations and Soils Report
You can file structural calculations, Title 24 calculations, soils reports, and related letters, e-mails, phone call notes, and meeting minutes in this folder.

113 Submittals—Shop Drawings and Samples
You can file submittals, including shop drawings, samples, related letters, e-mails, phone call notes, and meeting minutes in this folder.

The **Design** folder can be subdivided into the following folders:

Preliminary Site Plan
Entitlement
Design Elevations
Photos, Sketches, and Perspectives

All the **administrative** items in these design folders can be transfer to the **"101 General Project"** folder when the project progresses to DD and CD phases.

The **CD** folder can be subdivided into the following folders:

Architectural
Consultants (which can be subdivided into the following folders: Civil, Soils, Landscape, Structural, Electrical, Mechanical, and Plumbing)
Fixture Plan (from the tenant)
Prototype (from the tenant)
Temp (for temporary files)

Each project should also have one or more job boxes (the typical box for 8½ x 11 inch copy paper). The boxes are used to hold submittals and samples.

One year after a project's substantial completion, you can throw away the samples, move the hard copies of your administrative files for this project from your steel filing cabinet, and put them in this job box. The project's specifications book should also be put into the box.

Make sure you **clearly mark the project number, project name, and destroy date for files** on the <u>outside</u> of the job box. This job box can then be put into your firm's storage.

Each state has its own requirements for an architect to keep a project's records. For example, some states require an architect keep a project's records for <u>10</u> years after its completion. You need to check with the architect registration board of your state to find out the exact requirements and comply with them.

Construction drawings for ongoing projects should be kept in the steel flat files. **One year after** a project's completion, you can put the drawings into a storage tube. Make sure you **clearly mark the project number, project name, and destroy date for files** on the <u>outside</u> of the storage tube. This storage tube can then be put into your firm's storage.

Chapter Two

Clients and Contracts

A. Architecture Is a People Business

Architecture is a <u>knowledge-based</u> and <u>service-orientated</u> profession. It is a People Business.

No matter how good you are as an architect, **people need to like you as a person** before they will give you their business. Therefore, your marketing effort should focus on building your client's <u>trust</u> and a long-lasting <u>relationship</u>.

Once your clients start to use you, you must always give them the best professional service and design possible to keep them happy. <u>If they are happy, they will come back to you again and again</u>. This is the right way to grow your business.

On another note, most people can be nice to their boss and their clients, but it is also very important for you to treat contractors, your consultants, your subordinates, manufacturers' representatives, and material vendors with respect. They are very important members of your team, and they provide valuable expertise and information. Without their help, you cannot have a successful project.

People can know your true character by observing how you treat your consultants, your subordinates, and vendors.

If you need your team members to do something, just tell them the result that you want and when you need it. Be available for any questions, check the result every now and then and at important milestones and after completion. <u>Do not try to force them to do it your way</u>. Each person has his/her own preference.

B. Marketing and Architectural Business

Architects need to have clients to stay in business. This is one of the most important elements for an architectural practice.

Firstly, you need to provide **excellent service and the highest quality design**, plans, and specifications.

Secondly, you **HAVE to market your architectural service in a PROPER way.** <u>Either your clients need to come to you or you have to go find your clients</u>. You should AL-

WAYS keep on marketing your architectural service. At least 30% of your time and effort should be spent on marketing.

Some marketing ideas:

Advertise in the yellow pages, newspaper or trade publications, frequent the trade shows that your clients attend, write articles in trade magazines, send out holiday greeting cards, bring goodies to your clients' offices, take your clients out for lunch, play golf with your clients, organize golf games and invite your clients, etc.

Whatever you do, **your goal is to increase the exposure of your firm.** You need your clients to remember your name and your firm's name, and you want them to call you when they have any architectural needs. **You also have to be there when they need you.**

Just be careful and not overdo the marketing. Do not become a pest to your clients. For example, calling the clients every week and keep asking for projects may make you sound like a telemarketer, and it is probably the easiest way to irritate your clients and make them angry. On the other hand, bringing goodies to your clients every few months may be a good way to keep in touch.

Remember, **people will buy from people they like.** For your clients to give you projects, they have to like you as a person to begin with.

C. Contracts: Time and Material Contract, Unit Price Contract, Percentage of Construction Cost Contract, Fixed Fee Contract, and Reimbursable Expenses

How to determine your fees:

There are several common ways to quote your fees for professional architectural services:

1. Time and Materials (T&M)

You charge your clients based on the time you spent at the hourly rate for your staff; i.e., $155 for the principals, $125 per hour for the project managers and senior designers, $95 for the senior drafters, $65 for administrative staff, etc.

Remember, the professional service rate that you charge your client should be at least 2.5 times the actual rate that you pay your staff. For example, if you pay your project manager $50 per hour, you need to charge your clients at least $125 per hour. This is because you have to pay the office rent, utilities, etc., and you need to make a profit to stay in business.

The actual cost of your materials (paper, traveling expenses, printing costs, phone cost, etc.) is often marked up by a certain percentage, i.e., 5%, or 10% or 15%, etc., and then billed to your clients.

The time and materials billing method is used when the scope of the architectural project is not clearly defined yet. For example, at the beginning of a project, you may have to lay out different design schemes and discuss them with your clients several times. Your clients may take one or more of the schemes to show them to their tenants and may come back with additional revisions. I have worked on a project that the site schematic design was revised <u>81</u> times based on the client's requests.

Sometimes your clients may request you to give them a quote based on T&M, not to exceed a certain amount. They want to control the project's budget and know how much they will spend on design fees.

It is important for you to define the "not to exceed" amount as an allowance. That is, if the project scope changes or you are about to exceed the allowance amount, you can request your clients for an allowance increase. This way, your clients can know roughly how much they will spend on the project, and you will not be burned by committing yourself to a fixed fee for an uncertain project scope.

2. Unit Price

You can also charge your clients based on the unit price, i.e., $2 per s.f. of the gross building area for producing a complete set of a major retail building's (20,000.00 s.f. minimum) construction drawings and specifications based on an approved design, and $3 per s.f. for a minor retail building (20,000 s.f or less), etc.

3. Percentage of Construction Cost

This is similar to the unit price method. The typical architectural fee is about 7% to 10% of the construction cost. This fee includes your structural, electrical, mechanical, and plumbing (SEMP) consultants' fees also.

4. Fixed Fee

You can also charge your clients a fixed fee. You can use any of the methods above or a combination of several of them to come up with a fixed fee. For example, you can use the unit price method to come up with a design fee, and then verify it with the percentage of construction cost method.

It is also very important for you to <u>clearly define your project's scope</u>, because you need to adjust your fee if the project scope changes.

It is important for you to have a signed contract BEFORE you do any work for your clients to avoid any misunderstanding. Some states (like California) actually require an architect to have a **<u>written</u> contract** BEFORE he can provide any architectural service, with a few exceptions. Check with your state's architect board to find out the exact requirements for your state.

5. Reimbursable

Reimbursable items are those items that a design firm pays for out of pocket to later be reimbursed by the client. These items are typically billed separately, and are normally marked up by a percentage. This percentage is set by the contract you signed with your clients. For example, many architectural firms mark up their reimbursable items by 15%, i.e., [actual cost] × [115%] = [amount billed to client]

D. Additional Service Request

When to Send It and How to Send It:

If the clients want additional work done after you have a signed contract, you can send in an **Additional Service Request.** Accumulate a few small additional service requests and send them in as one request. <u>Do not nickel and dime your clients</u>. It is one of the easiest ways to make your client angry.

Perhaps some small additional service fees can be absorbed or merged into larger ones to keep the client happy and ensure repeat business.

You may want to call your clients and verbally discuss the potential additional service requests before you actually write one up. Make sure you explain the additional work clearly. Nobody wants to pay extra, but if you clearly explain why the work is beyond the original scope, most clients will pay it.

E. Task Log and Field/City Visit Log

After a while, the number of additional services can become large and confusing. It is a great idea to use a task log to track all the tasks for your project, including tasks under original contract and the tasks under additional service requests.

The following is a sample **task log**:

Table 2.1   Sample Task Log

Task Log for Major Building A for American Retail, Inc.
Located at City of Anywhere, CA, USA

A+A Job #: 09388   **Rev. Date: 9/6/09**

Task #	Description of Work/Changes	Arch (A+A)	Struct. (ABF)	Elect. (EGL)	Mech. (MSI)	Plumb. (PBI)	Amount Unsigned	Amount Signed	Date Signed	Remark/ History
100	Create a "dummy" submittal set for Major Building A based on a similar set done before	$14,860	$2,148	$1,200	$600	$1,200	0	$20,008	1/7/2009	
101	Design Development	$5,000	0	0	0	0	0	$5,000	7/25/2008	Basic contract
200	Major Building A Shell buildable set without TI coordination	$18,500	$4,100	$1,000	$800	$800		$25,200	7/25/2008	Basic contract
201	Create color elev.-voided	0	0	0	0	0	0	0		
202	Update per tenant lease exhibit	$2,000	0	0	0	0	0	$2,000	1/10/2009	
203	Major Building A TI per tenant prototype	$18,350	0	$600	0	0	0	$18,950	4/11/2009	
204	Update to new tenant prototype per tenant markup only	$4,915	0	$900	$300	$250	0	$6,365	6/23/2009	
205	Update plans per revised fixture plan F-1 & F-2 revised on 5/26/08	$3,130	0	$1,200	0	0		$4,330	7/27/2009	
206	Adding steel lattice	$3,500	0	0	0	0	$3,500	0		
250	On-site visit per diem $1,200 x 12 = $14,400	$14,600	0	0	0	0	0	$14,600	7/25/2008	Basic contract
999	Reimbursable expenses									Basic contract
Sub-total		$84,855	$6,248	$4,900	$1,700	$2,250	$3,500	$96,453		

Note: A+A is the architect, ABF is the structural engineer, MSI is the mechanical engineer, PBI is the plumbing engineer, and EGL is the electrical engineer.

Because city visits and field visits are often billed based on the number of the trips, it is important to keep a good **Field/City Visit Log.**

The following is a sample **Field/City Visit Log:**

Table 2.2   Sample Field/City Visit Log

Field/City Visit Log for Major Building A for American Retail, Inc.
Located at City of Anywhere, CA, USA

A+A Job #: 09388   Rev. Date: 9/8/09

Task 900

Name	Date	Purpose	Fee	Reimbursable
Architect's trips:				
Gang Chen of A+A	1/18/2008	City meeting per the request of client	$1,000	1.15 x actual cost per contract
Gang Chen of A+A	3/22/2008	Site meeting per the request of client	$1,000	1.15 x actual cost per contract
Consultants' trips:				
Bill Williams of EGL	3/22/2008	Site meeting per the request of client	$1,000	1.15 x actual cost per contract
Total billing			**$3,000**	**1.15 x actual cost per contract**

Note: *A+A is the architect, ABF is the structural engineer, MSI is the mechanical engineer, PBI is the plumbing engineer, and EGL is the electrical engineer.*

Chapter Three

Pre-Design, Entitlement, Governing Agencies, Project Program, Planning, and Preliminary & Schematic Design

A. Project Contact List

At the beginning of your project, you want to set up a Project Contact List. You can put all the related parties' contact information for the project on this list. The following is a sample Project Contact List. Since most of the time people communicate with each other via phone or e-mails, I place the phone numbers and e-mail addresses closer to the name and make the contact list easy to use. Not every entity listed will be involved in a project. I use **bold font** for the entities that are frequently involved in a project.

Table 3.1   Sample Project Contact List

**Project Contact List for Major Building A for American Retail, Inc.
Located at City of Anywhere, CA, USA**

A+A Job #: 09388   Rev. Date: 7/8/09

Entity	Contact	Phone/Fax/E-mail	Name and Address
Client		Office: Fax: E-mail:	
Architect	Gang Chen	Office: (123) 555-1216 Cell: (123) 555-1226 Fax: (123) 555-1218 (The numbers above are fictitious, for demonstration purposes only) E-mail: plantingdesign@yahoo.com	A+A, Inc. 126 Main St., Suite B City of Anywhere, CA USA (The address above is fictitious, for demon-stration purposes only)
Governing Agency (Planning Dept.)		Office: Fax: E-mail:	
Governing Agency (Building Dept.)		Office: Fax: E-mail:	
Governing Agency (Fire Dept.)		Office: Fax: E-mail:	
Governing Agency (County Health Dept.—Health dept.		Office: Fax: E-mail:	

plan check is required if the building occupant will sell food, including prepackaged food like candies)			
Governing Agency (Public Works Dept.)		Office: Fax: E-mail:	
Governing Agency (Waste Management Dept.)		Office: Fax: E-mail:	
Governing Agency (School District—For determining school fees, often based on a fee table or formula per s.f. of the building)		Office: Fax: E-mail:	
Utility Company (Telephone)		Office: Fax: E-mail:	
Utility Company (Cable)		Office: Fax: E-mail:	
Utility Company (Water)		Office: Fax: E-mail:	
Utility Company (Power)		Office: Fax: E-mail:	
Consultant (Soils Engineer)		Office: Fax: E-mail:	
Consultant (Civil Engineer)		Office: Fax: E-mail:	
Consultant (Traffic Engineer)		Office: Fax: E-mail:	
Consultant (Landscape Architect)		Office: Fax: E-mail:	
Consultant (Structural Engineer)		Office: Fax: E-mail:	
Consultant (Electrical Engineer)		Office: Fax: E-mail:	
Consultant (Mechanical Engineer)		Office: Fax: E-mail:	
Consultant (Electrical Engineer)		Office: Fax: E-mail:	

Consultant (Plumbing Engineer)		Office: Fax: E-mail:	
Consultant (Signage Consultant)		Office: Fax: E-mail:	
Consultant (Refrigeration Engineer)		Office: Fax: E-mail:	
Consultant (Fire Sprinkler Engineer)		Office: Fax: E-mail:	
Consultant often hired by owner directly (Roofing Consultant)		Office: Fax: E-mail:	
Consultant often hired by owner directly (Lighting Consultant)		Office: Fax: E-mail:	
Consultant often hired by owner directly (Decoration/Decor Consultant)		Office: Fax: E-mail:	
General Contractor (Building)		Office: Fax: E-mail:	
General Contractor (Building—Job Site)		Office: Fax: E-mail:	
General Contractor (Site)		Office: Fax: E-mail:	
General Contractor (Site—Job Site)		Office: Fax: E-mail:	
Tenant		Office: Fax: E-mail:	
Tenant's Architect		Office: Fax: E-mail:	
Tenant's Signage Consultant		Office: Fax: E-mail:	
Tenant's Soils Engineer		Office: Fax: E-mail:	

B. Pre-Design Items

Your clients normally will provide you some materials at the beginning of the project, including, but not limited to: site survey (typically an **ALTA** survey), title report & soils report.

*Note: A unit used frequently to note site areas in a site survey or site plan is **acre**, while your building areas are measured in s.f., so you have to convert site area from acres into s.f. constantly to calculate site building coverage, floor area ratio, parking count, landscape area ratio, etc. You need to memorize this important fact: **1 acre = 43,560 s.f.** (**Mnemonics:** 4 + 3 = 7, 5 + 6 = 11. So, if you can remember **7/11**, then you can remember **43,560 s.f.**)*

ALTA means **American Land Title Association.** It is the national trade association of the **abstract and title insurance industry** and was founded in 1907. An **abstracter** is the person who prepares a summary (or **abstract**) of public records relating to a title to a specific parcel of land. An **abstract** can also be defined as the history of the title.

ALTA's official website is:
http://www.alta.org/

ACSM is the **American Congress on Surveying & Mapping.** It is a nonprofit educational organization to advance the sciences of surveying and mapping and related fields and was founded in 1941.

ACSM's official website is:
http://www.acsm.net/

An **ALTA survey** is a boundary survey based on a set of minimum standards that are adopted by the **ALTA/ACSM.** It shows rights-of-way, easement, improvements, encroachments, encumbrances, and other elements related to land ownership. It is often used for commercial properties and meets a high standard. It is often done by a civil engineer or a surveyor hired by the owner directly.

ALTA surveys cannot be completed without a current title commitment. The surveyor needs title commitment for the legal description of encumbrances and the property.

CLTA is the **California Land Title Association**, a nonprofit corporation founded in 1907.

CLTA's official website is:
http://www.clta.org/

An ALTA title insurance is typically more expensive than a CLTA title insurance, because it covers all the standard items that CLTA covers (title to the real property, defects, liens, and encumbrances, marketable interests in the real property, lack of a right of access to and from the real property, and forgeries or failed conveyances in the chain of title), plus the following:

Matters that can be discovered by a survey, and easements, discrepancies, encroachments, or conflicts in boundary lines not shown by the public records.

A **title report** is a written description of the title status of a real property. It usually includes how the title is held and names of titleholders, property description, encumbrances, tax rates, and real property taxes due. **A preliminary report** is a title report provided when the report is ordered, and **a final title report** is an up-to-date title report provided at the time of recording. A title report can be prepared by an abstractor, an attorney, a title company, or an escrow company.

Soils reports, or "geotechnical soils reports," or "geotechnical investigation reports," are prepared by a licensed civil engineer or a geotechnical engineer experienced in soils engineering. They provide earth conditions affecting a building. Most new building constructions will require a soils report, especially in areas with low strength or expansive soils, projects on steep slopes, or FEMA floodplains or areas with high groundwater, projects where the foundation will be supported by fill or projects with a lot of grading.

Architects and structural engineers will need to review the soils report and **pay special attention to,** and follow, the **recommendations** on what kind of slab and footing to use, and what kind of base and moisture barrier to use under them. For example, a soils report may recommend a 4" slab with #3 rebar at 24" each way, over 2" sand over **15 mil** (thick) moisture barrier over another 2" of sand, and 12" wide minimum x 24" wide minimum continuous footing.

Note:
1. *A "mil" equals to 1/1000 of an inch,* 15 mil = 15 x 1/1000 = 0.015 inches.
2. *A #3 rebar means a rebar with a 3 x ⅛" diameter, and a #5 rebar means a rebar with a 5 x ⅛" diameter, and so on.*

In most cases, a soils report is completed before the developer can finalize the lease with the tenants.

Some clients, especially **some national retail tenants, do not like to have sand over the moisture barrier,** because they do not want to have moisture trapped in the sand between the moisture barrier and the concrete slab. They prefer recommendation like: 5" slab with #3 rebar at 24" each way, over **15 mil** moisture barrier **over 6" of crushed rocks**, and 12" wide minimum x 24" wide minimum continuous footing. Please note that if you are using this option, you need to use **at least 15 mil** thick instead of a **6 mil** or **10 mil** thick moisture barrier, otherwise it may be too thin and may be penetrated by the crushed rocks below.

You also have to go back to your geotechnical or civil engineer to find out if they can adjust the soils report to meet the tenant's criteria.

Try to get the tenant's criteria before the soils investigation is done and forward the tenant's criteria to your geotechnical or civil engineer right away to avoid delay and confusion in the project.

Common methods used to obtain geotechnical data and create a soils report include <u>test pits, core samples, seismograph, and steel rods</u> driven into the soil to detect the presence of rock and test density.

C. Entitlement

1. Definition

Entitlement means a right granted. In architecture and land development, the **Entitlement Process** means the legal way of gaining approval for the <u>right</u> to develop a property <u>for a specific use</u>.

For example, a developer may buy a piece of empty land and entitle it for a <u>commercial</u> use, and then sell it to someone else for a profit. Once a land is entitled for commercial use, its value may double or even triple.

2. Your Responsibilities as an Architect

As an architect, you can assist the developer to handle the **Entitlement Process**. Most architects charge this service <u>on a T&M basis</u> because the scope of the project is often <u>not</u> clearly defined, and there are <u>uncertainties</u> when dealing with governing agencies.

You need to contact the governing agencies and get a list of required items for entitlement submittal. You probably need to provide an overall preliminary building design elevation and a preliminary design site plan, and contact the developer to obtain the site survey, **Environmental Impact Report** (EIR), and **Title Report** done by other consultants, and contact the utility companies for existing <u>utility plans</u> and information. You will probably need to assemble the **Entitlement Package** and put everything together.

D. Governing Agencies

In the U.S., most states and cities adapted the ***International Building Codes*** (IBC), but they also have their own special requirements.

At the beginning of the project, you need to check the city's website or call the various departments of the cities to do a quick code research. The codes that affect architectural design are typically part of the city's **municipal codes**, like parking requirements, setback requirements, landscape requirements, etc. You can simply download a copy of the **municipal codes** and read it. You can also call the various departments of the cities if you need help locating the information or if you have additional questions.

1. Planning Department Checklist & Submittal Requirements

Note: *Not every item on the list applies to your project. You can probably download standard exhibits or diagrams from the planning department's website or check the* *municipal codes at your city's website to get responses to most of the questions below:*

1) Planning department's **website** address. Whom did you talk to? What is his/her name, e-mail, and phone number? Did you confirm your conversation in writing via an e-mail or fax? Make sure you keep the fax confirmation sheet in your files.
2) Is your project site part of the city's **specific plan area**?
3) What is your site's land use **zoning**?
4) **Building setback** requirements: front yard setback, side yard setback, backyard setback. Will pilasters, trellises, or canopies be allowed in setback area?

*Note: Check your survey map or title report or check with your civil engineer or the utility companies to find out if your site has any **easement requirements**, and determine if you can build within the easement. Some easements will not allow you to build at all, while other easements may allow you to build small structures with a maximum footing depth, or will allow you to build sidewalks or curbs or parking stalls. You need to find out the exact requirements.*

5) Do you need to **dedicate** part of your site as a public sitewalk to the city?
6) What is the **maximum height** that you can build?

Note: Please check the IBC or your locally adopted version of IBC to find out what the <u>maximum height</u> and <u>basic allowable area</u> and <u>allowable area increase</u> is for your building per codes.

7) Are there any special requirements on the style or look of the architecture for your site area?
8) What is the **Floor Area Ratio (FAR)**?

*Note: **Floor Area Ratio** is the total floor area of the buildings <u>divided</u> by the site area. Your city often has a <u>maximum FAR</u> allowed for your site.*

9) What is **site coverage** requirement? I.e., the maximum percentage of site area that can be covered by your building. <u>50%</u> is common.
10) What is the **parking ratio**? **Note:** Most cities require retail buildings have <u>4 or 5 parking stalls per 1,000 s.f.</u> They also typically require restaurants and theaters to have more parking stalls. Some cities will let you have fewer parking stalls if you provide bike or motorcycle parking spaces
11) What is the <u>standard</u> parking stall size? (<u>8' x 18' or 9' x 19'</u> is common)
12) What is the <u>compact</u> parking stall size? (<u>7' x 15' or 8' x 16'</u> is common)
13) What is the <u>percentage of compact</u> parking stalls allowed? Generally, <u>20% or 25%</u> is common.
14) Will car front **overhang** be allowed?

Note: Most cities will allow <u>2' overhang</u> over sitewalk or planter. If you are counting on the 2' overhang over the sidewalk to make the parking stall size re-

quired, make sure you still have the minimum width of the sitewalk as required by handicap codes (typically 4' min.) and the local codes. Generally, 5' or 6' wide sidewalk is common.

15) You need to check the **handicap codes** and the city's codes (for special handicap requirements) for the minimum number and size of handicap parking stalls required and the number and size of van-accessible handicap parking stalls required.

16) What is the minimum **drive aisle width** for one-way drive, two-way drive, and entry drive?

17) Will **angled** parking (45 degree, 60 degree, etc.) stalls be allowed? What are the parking stalls and drive aisle requirements for angled parking?

18) Will the parking stalls need double stripes or single stripes?

19) What are the **landscape coverage** requirements? What percentage of the gross site area should be a landscape area? What percentage of the net parking area should be a landscape area?

Some cities require a minimum **percentage** (like 8% or 10% or 15%, etc.) of the site to be a landscape area, and sometimes sidewalks or other hardscape can be counted as landscape area (but not to exceed a certain percentage of the landscape area, like 20%).

Some cities may require a certain percentage (like 25% or 50%) of the parking area to have **shade** provided by trees. You may also get a **LEED point** for providing shade for 50% or more of the parking area.

Some cities may require one tree for a certain number of stalls, like one tree for every six parking stalls, etc.

20) What are the **landscape setback** requirements for side streets and for front streets? (For example, 10', 20', or 30' from sitewalk, etc.)

21) What is the minimum width for a landscape island or a landscape "finger"? Generally, 5' is common.

22) What is the minimum **turning radius** for curbs?

23) Do you need to provide **screen walls** for rooftop equipment?

24) Do you need to provide screen walls for parking stalls facing the street? If required, 3' high screen walls are common. Do you need to provide screen walls for transformers or loading docks?

25) Does your **trash enclosure** need to match the building's finish? What is the minimum height for your trash enclosure? Generally, 6' is common. Does it need landscape screening? Does it need a trellis or cover? Does its trellis or cover need to be fire-rated if it is adjacent to a building? Some cities require its trellis or cover to be 1-hour rated.

26) What is the maximum height of lettering for **building signage**? What is the maximum signage area allowed per elevation? Generally, 200 s.f. is common. Will the city allow signage for all elevations or only 1, 2, or 3 elevations? What are the requirements for **monument signs or pylon signs**?

Some cities will allow your building a certain s.f. of building signage area <u>per linear foot of frontage</u> of elevation. They also will typically give you a maximum s.f. of signage area allowed per elevation.

For example, if a city allows your building to have 2 s.f. of building signage area per linear foot of frontage of elevation, and a maximum of 200 s.f. signage area allowed per elevation, you have 80 linear feet of frontage for your south elevation, so you can have 2 x 80 = 160 s.f. < 200 s.f. You can have 160 s.f. (NOT 200 s.f.) of TOTAL signage area for your south elevation.

27) What is the maximum height for **light poles**? Is there a standard design for a light pole base?
28) What is the minimum and maximum footcandle required for **site lighting**? You can have your **electrical engineer** contact the city regarding this.
29) Have your **civil engineer** contact the city's public works department or engineering department regarding **off-site** requirements if your project has any off-site work.
30) What are the **submittal requirements?** <u>How many</u> sets of plans do you need to submit? Generally, <u>one</u> or two sets for the planning department are common. Get the application form and submittal requirements and list from the city, if possible. How much is the plan check <u>fee</u>? Is there a fee table? What is the <u>turnaround time</u> for a plan check?
31) Do you need to submit for a Planning Department <u>Staff Review</u> or <u>Design Review Board</u> **(DRB)** review or a <u>City Council Review</u> or <u>Planning Commission Review</u>? Do you need to apply for a <u>Conditional Use Permit</u> **(CUP)**? Do you need to apply for a zoning change? Does your project comply with the city's **general plan** and **specific plan**?
32) Do you need to have an <u>Environmental Impact Report</u> **(EIR)**?

Note: You should <u>ALWAYS call and confirm ALL submittal requirements</u>, especially <u>plan check fees</u> required for submittal, even if you may be able to get the information from the governing agency's website because the information on the website may be incomplete or outdated. Please also <u>confirm</u> your phone conversation with the staff at the governing agency <u>in writing</u> via an e-mail or fax. You do not want to request a check from your client and then find out you need to pay more for the city to accept your plans. That will make you look like an idiot who does not know what s/he is doing.

2. Building Department Checklist & Submittal Requirements

Note: Not every item on the list applies to your project. You can probably download standard exhibits or diagrams from the building department's website or check the municipal codes at your city's website to get the responses to most of the questions below:

1) What is the building department's **website** address? Whom did you talk to? What is his/her name, e-mail, and phone number? Did you confirm your conversation via an e-mail or fax?

2) What are the current versions of codes being used? For example, 2007 CBC, 2007 CMC, 2007 CPC, 2005 NEC, etc.

3) Are there local amendments for building codes? Any local ordinance and municipal codes?

4) Are there any expected revisions or updates to the codes?

5) Will pilasters or canopies be included in the building area?

6) Coordinate with the city and do a **preliminary building qualification:** determine what type of building you are building (Type I-A, Type V-B, etc.), what the basic allowable area is, what the city's definition of side yards is and how they are measured, what kinds of allowable area increase are available, if you can use 60' side yards on all sides to build an unlimited building, if you need to submit reciprocal lease agreements from all tenants to maintain the 60' side yards, etc.

7) What are the **submittal requirements?** How many sets of plans, calculations and soils reports do you need to submit? Three sets of plans, two sets of structural calculations, two sets of T-24 energy calculations for California projects, and two sets of soils reports for the building department are common. Get the application form and submittal requirements and list from the city, if possible. How much is the plan check fee? Is there a fee table? Do you need to pay a school fee, a sewage connection fee, etc.? How much? Can you pay the combined plan check fees for the planning department, building department, and fire department in one check? What is the turnaround time for a plan check?

8) Will the city accept the first submittal without a wet stamp and wet signature? Will the city accept an electronic stamp and signature? In California, the California Architect Board allows architects to submit plans with an electronic stamp and signature, but you need to confirm with the city and make sure they accept this first.

9) Do you need to bind architectural, structural, electrical, mechanical, and plumbing plans together for each set, or do you need to keep them separate and submit them to different plan checkers? I.e., architectural and structural plans for a building plan checker, electrical plans for an electrical plan checker, mechanical and plumbing plans for the mechanical and plumbing plan checker?

10) Do you need to make a separate submittal to the fire department and a separate submittal to the health department? Sometimes the fire department is a county agency instead of a city agency. Health departments are typically a county agency instead of a city agency, and normally require a separate submittal and a separate check for a plan check fee.

11) Can you mail or overnight the plans for submittal to the city?

12) Can you get an expedited plan check? Do you need to pay extra? How much? Is the plan check done in-house or by an outside plan checker?

Note: You should ALWAYS call and confirm ALL submittal requirements, especially plan check fees required for submittal, even if you may be able to get the information from the governing agency's website because the information on the website may be incomplete or outdated. Please also confirm your phone conversation with the staff at the governing agency in writing via an e-mail or fax. You do not want to request a check from your client and then find out you need to pay more for the city to accept your plans. That will make you look like an idiot who does not know what s/he is doing.

3. Fire Department Checklist & Submittal Requirements

Note: Not every item on the list applies to your project. You can probably download standard exhibits or diagrams from the fire department's website or check the municipal codes at your city's website to get the responses to most of the questions below:

1) What is the fire department's **website** address? Whom did you talk to? What is his/her name, e-mail, and phone number? Did you confirm your conversation via an e-mail or fax?
2) What are the current versions of codes being used?
3) Are there local code amendments, ordinances, and municipal codes?
4) Are there any expected revisions or updates to the codes?
5) What are the minimum entry drive and on-site drive widths and turning radius for fire truck lanes? Do you need to paint the fire lane curbs red and paint them with special lettering? Where are the locations and the wording and size of the lettering?
6) Shall the fire department connection (FDC) be located in the back of the building OR in front of the building?
7) When will a building need to be fire-sprinklered? When its area reaches a minimum size?
8) What are the **submittal requirements?** How many sets of plans do you need to submit? One set for the fire department is common. It can often be submitted to the building department and then routed to the fire department. Please confirm this information with the city. Get the application form and submittal requirements and list from the fire department, if possible. How much is the plan check fee? Is there a fee table? What is the turnaround time for a plan check?
9) Can you mail or overnight the plans for submittal to the fire department?
10) Can you get an expedited plan check? Do you need to pay extra? How much? Is the plan check done in-house or by an outside plan checker?

Note: You should ALWAYS call and confirm ALL submittal requirements, especially the plan check fees required for submittal, even if you may be able to get the information from the governing agency's website because the information on the website may be incomplete or outdated. Please also confirm your phone conversation with the staff at the governing agency in writing via an e-mail or fax. You do not want to request a check from your client and then find out you need to pay more for the city to accept your plans. That will make you look like an idiot who does not know what s/he is doing.

4. Health Department Checklist & Submittal Requirements

Note: Not every item on the list applies to your project. You can probably download standard exhibits or diagrams from the health department's website to get a response to most of the questions below:

1) What is the health department's **website** address? Whom did you talk to? What is his/her name, e-mail, and phone number? Did you <u>confirm your conversation</u> via an e-mail or fax?
2) Are there special requirements for the floor and wall in bathrooms and at food prep areas? What are the requirements?

   Note: Many health departments have the following requirements for bathrooms and janitors' rooms in retail buildings that process foods or sell prepackaged foods (like candies):

   a. The VCT flooring is not acceptable.
   b. 4'-0" high or 8'-0" high FRP or ceramic tile wall finish (call your health department to find out the exact requirements)
   c. The following flooring and base are acceptable:
       a) A ceramic tile **<u>floor</u>** with a **6" high** continuous ceramic tile **cove base.**

       OR

       b) A **sealed** concrete <u>floor</u> with a 6" high ceramic tile with a **slim foot base.**

       OR

       c) A **<u>sheet</u> vinyl** floor with a 6" **continuous wrap-up base.**

3) What are the **submittal requirements?** <u>How many</u> sets of plans do you need to submit? One set for the health department is common. In some cities, it can be submitted to the building department and then routed to the health department. Please confirm with the city. Get the application form and submittal requirements and the list from the health department, if possible. How much is the plan check <u>fee</u>? Is there a <u>fee table</u>? What is the <u>turnaround time</u> for a plan check?
4) Can you <u>mail or overnight</u> the plans for submittal to the health department?
5) Can you get an <u>expedited</u> plan check? Do you need to pay extra? How much? Is the plan check done <u>in-house</u> or by an outside plan checker?

   Note: You should <u>ALWAYS call and confirm ALL submittal requirements</u>, especially <u>plan check fees</u> required for submittal, even if you may be able to get the information from the governing agency's website because the information on the website may be incomplete or outdated. Please <u>confirm</u> your phone conversation with the staff at the governing agency <u>in writing</u> via an e-mail or fax. You do not want to request a check from your client and then find out you need to pay more *for the city to accept your plans. That will make you look like an idiot who does not know what s/he is doing.*

E. Project Program, Planning, Preliminary Design, Conceptual/Schematic Design, and Color & Material Boards

1. Project Program

Your client can provide the project program, or you and your client can develop it together. It may include the project budget, objectives, functions, and relationships between these functions and spatial needs, as well as design expectations.

2. Planning

Arrange the building(s) on the site to fully take advantage of the <u>dominant wind</u>, sun, shadow, <u>solar orientation</u>, site opportunities and constraints, and pedestrian and vehicular <u>traffic flow</u> to reach the full potential of the site and achieve the maximum benefits and efficiency, and provide <u>phasing plans</u>, if necessary.

It is a good idea to get your client's <u>written approval BEFORE</u> you move on to the next step of the project.

3. Preliminary Design

Provide generic <u>site layout</u> and sketch <u>options</u>. You may use one or more of the following means to convey a "<u>theme</u>," or "<u>feel</u>," for the project: hand or computer <u>sketches</u>, <u>image boards</u>, <u>special details</u>, <u>clip arts</u>, <u>elevations</u>, and <u>color and material boards</u>.

It is a good idea to get your client's <u>written approval BEFORE</u> you move on to the next step of the project.

4. Conceptual/Schematic Design

Prepare and present various <u>design alternatives</u> to the client for review, comment, and approval; provide one set of schematic floor plans drawn to scale to show the building <u>layout</u>, <u>overall size for the plan</u>, and <u>room sizes</u>; provide elevations to show the design <u>character</u> and overall <u>appearance</u>; call out <u>material and colors</u>. You may offer your client a statement of <u>probable construction costs</u> upon his/her request.

It is a good idea to get your client's <u>written approval BEFORE</u> you move on to the next step of the project.

5. Color & Material Boards

<u>Color and material boards</u> are a very important means to communicate your design concept. Some city planning departments or tenants may require <u>color and material boards</u> as part of your submittal package. It is a good way to show the true color and texture of the materials used in your project. It is always a good idea to take photos of your <u>color and material boards</u> for your files and <u>send a copy to the job site</u> for the contractors' reference to avoid major errors in color and materials. This is based on experience.

Chapter Four

Design Development (DD) & Project Schedule

A. Design Development

Design Development is the further development of your design after your conceptual/schematic design is accepted and approved by your client. In the design development phase, you will help the client to establish all major building elements and outline specifications, materials, methods, and major building systems, including structural and mechanical systems and construction type and standards. You will also provide floor plans, elevations, sections, and some details with accurate and major dimensions to define areas and spaces, and submit design development drawings to your client for review, comment, and approval. You may also offer your client a revised statement of **probable construction costs** upon his/her request.

It is a good idea to get your client's written approval BEFORE you move on to the next step of the project.

Some architectural offices skip the step of **Design Development,** and move directly from Conceptual/Schematic Design to the Construction Documents Phase.

B. Project Schedule

Your client may request you to provide a project schedule at the beginning of the project or at any other stage of the project. For you, it is easier to come up with a project schedule at the design development stage because you already know the materials, methods, major building systems (including structural and mechanical systems), and construction type and standards for your project. You should have a clear understanding of the project timeframe by now.

As long as you know how much time you need for each phase of the project, you can easily come up with a project schedule with **Microsoft Project** software.

The following are the major phases and activities for each phase and some estimate times to assist you to come up with a project schedule. Not all steps and phases are necessary. Contact your governing agencies to confirm.

1. Entitlement and Design

1) Produce a design submittal package for the city, including overall building elevations, preliminary site plans, and landscape plans. It normally takes 3 to 4 weeks. Verify with the city regarding the exact requirements for the design submittal package because its content will affect the schedule.

2) The client's review of your design submittal package normally takes 2 to 3 weeks.

3) The city planning department staff will review your design submittal package. It normally takes 2 to 3 weeks. Please verify with the city regarding the exact turnaround time.

4) Review by Design Review Board (DRB) or Architectural Review Committee (ARC). You normally need to go through this step before you can present to the planning commission. You need to contact the planning department to find out the schedule and date for DRB or ARC meetings and update your schedule accordingly.

5) Review by the city's planning commission. You need to contact the planning department to find out the schedule and date for planning commission meetings and update your schedule accordingly.

6) Review by the city council. You need to contact the planning department to find out the schedule and date for city council meetings and update your schedule accordingly.

7) Design appeal period. It normally takes 2 to 3 weeks. You need to contact the planning department to confirm and update your schedule accordingly.

2. Design Development

1) It normally takes 3 to 4 weeks.
2) This step can be omitted.

3. Construction Documents

a. Site Development Construction Documents

1) Coordinate with the civil engineer to come up with a base site plan for site architectural, landscape, and electrical plans. It normally takes 2 to 3 weeks.

2) Produce site construction documents, including your plans and the consultants' plans. It normally takes 4 to 6 weeks. You need to contact the consultants to confirm and update your schedule accordingly.

3) Review by governing agencies and clients. They can occur concurrently and normally take 2 to 3 weeks. You need to contact governing agencies to confirm and update your schedule accordingly.

Note: Civil plans are normally submitted separately by the civil engineer to the public works department.

4) Update plans per <u>plan check correction</u> list and <u>client's comments</u>. It normally takes 2 to 3 weeks.
5) The 2nd plan check by governing agencies. It normally takes 2 to 3 weeks.
6) Permit ready.

b. Building Construction Documents

This can be <u>concurrent</u> with the site development construction documents.

1) Coordinate with your client and consultants to come up with the <u>base plans</u> for building architectural, structural, electrical plans, mechanical, and plumbing plans. It normally takes 2 to 3 weeks.
2) Produce <u>building construction documents</u>, including your plans and the consultants' plans. It normally takes 6 to 8 weeks. You need to contact the consultants to confirm and update your schedule accordingly.
3) Review by <u>governing agencies</u> and <u>clients</u>. They can occur concurrently and normally take 2 to 3 weeks. You need to contact governing agencies to confirm and update your schedule accordingly.
4) Update plans per <u>plan check correction list</u> and <u>client's comments</u>. It normally takes 2 to 3 weeks.
5) The 2nd plan check by governing agencies. It normally takes 2 to 3 weeks.
6) Permit ready.

4. Bidding and Negotiation

1) Bidding normally takes 3 to 4 weeks.
2) Negotiation and awarding the contract normally takes 1 week.

5. Site and Building Construction

1) It normally takes 3 to 4 weeks to get a <u>certified pad</u>. This need to happen <u>before</u> the building permit is ready.
2) Construction normally takes 26 to 28 weeks for retail buildings. It can take longer for other building types.

Chapter Five

Construction Documents (CD)

A. General Information

Construction documents include construction drawings, specifications, addenda, bulletins, etc. They are used by the contractors to bid or price the project, and they are used to obtain a building permit. Most of your actual design work will be done at the CD stage.

If you are working on a large site with multiple buildings, you may want to break the CD sets into a **site development CD set** and various **building CD sets**.

A building CD set can be further divided into a building shell CD set and a building tenant improvement (TI) CD set. A building shell CD set can be a Raw Building Shell CD set or a Vanilla Building Shell CD set.

Raw Shell or **Dark Shell** CD sets will not show any interior finish, no bathrooms, no interior ductwork, and sometimes no rooftop HVAC units. Water, sewer, and storm drain lines are brought to within 5' of the building's exterior walls.

Vanilla Shell or **White Shell** CD sets will show basic drywall taped, sanded, and ready for paint, typical 2' x 4' T-bar ceiling with lights, minimum and typical bathrooms per codes, basic interior ductwork, and rooftop HVAC units.

Some people also use the term **Grey Shell**. **Grey Shell** is the shell between **Dark Shell** and **White Shell**. It is similar to Dark Shell, but probably has a rooftop HVAC unit and simple HVAC ductwork that drops down to the space.

These terms have different meanings to different developers. It is a good idea for you to send out a simple questionnaire to confirm the exact definitions of these terms with your clients.

The advantage of producing a site development CD set as a separate submittal is:

Once it is approved, the GC can start to do site development for the entire site and just leave out the building pads for the buildings that are not ready for construction. The landscape, hardscape, trash enclosure, trellis, benches, trashcans, ashtrays, etc., will be designed consistently throughout the site. This will expedite the construction of the entire site and buildings.

You can then submit each building and adjacent area as a separate CD set later.

If you are working on a small site with one or two buildings, you can combine the site development and building CD drawings as one set.

Construction documents will be included as part of the contract documents. They are legal contracts between the owner and the contractor.

First, you want to create a set of construction documents that are as <u>comprehensive and accurate</u> as possible.

Second, <u>nobody is perfect</u>, and NOBODY can create a perfect set of construction documents. You want your construction documents to at least meet the <u>industry standard</u> and the quality of work expected in your <u>local area</u>.

B. Building Construction Drawings

Construction drawings show <u>locations, quantity</u>, and <u>sizes</u> of project elements.

We are going to tell you <u>how to set up</u> the drawings set, <u>what</u> information shall go on each sheet, and <u>what to look for</u> when you do your coordination for both architectural and consultant drawings. It may be a good idea for you to obtain a good <u>sample construction drawing set</u> and refer to it as we discuss this subject. You can also start to set up a good construction drawing set for yourself. Once you set it up, you can simply <u>save as, revise, and reuse</u> the set for your other projects. This is the power of the computer. This is how you can become <u>efficient and profitable</u> in your architectural business.

1. Setting up the Drawing Sheet and Title Block for Your Construction Drawings Set

There are three commonly used paper sizes for construction drawings: <u>24" x 36", 30" x 42"</u>, and <u>36" x 48"</u>. The 36" x 48" sheet size is used for projects with a large building floor plan.

See the link below for a comprehensive discussion of paper size:
http://en.wikipedia.org/wiki/Paper_size

Before you start to set up a construction drawings set, you need to contact the governing agencies for your project to confirm the sheet sizes that are acceptable to them.

First, you need to set up a sheet border and a title block. In many firms, this step has probably already been done by someone else. However, I discuss it here in case you need to do this at a small firm or for your own firm.

You can use a number of computer software programs for producing construction drawings, but the dominant software in the construction industry in the U.S. is AutoCAD. Our discussion will be based on AutoCAD. I am not going to discuss every detail. Instead, I shall focus on the content that can be most helpful to you.

You want to define your sheet size in the computer:

Some people use the non-plot "defpoints" layer in AutoCAD to draw the 24" x 36", 30" x 42", or 36" x 48" sheet. This may create problems in plotting: part of your sheet border will be cut off when you plot.

Some people use a separate layer and a very fine pen weight to draw the sheet. This is not a good idea either, because the line defining the sheet size will show up outside of your drawing borderline, and it does not look good.

The correct way is to define your sheet with dots or a small "L" shape line at the four corners of your sheet. You can pick the centers of these dots or the intersections of the small "L" shape lines to plot. It will give you the correct sheet size, but the sheet line will NOT show up on your plots. Make sure you set up the lower left-hand corner of your sheet at point (0, 0) in your computer.

Most offices set up the sheet border and the title block at paper space and draw the building elements at model space. ALL dimensions should be real dimensions when you draw with AutoCAD for both paper space and model space.

You want to make sure you leave enough distance between your sheet edge and your sheet borderline so that your borderline will not be cut off when you plot the sheet. One way to set up the sheet is to leave ⅝" (½" may NOT be enough) distance between your sheet edge and your sheet border line at top, bottom, and right-hand side of the sheet, and leave 2" distance between your sheet edge and your sheet border line at the left-hand side of the sheet. You leave extra space on the left so that you will have room to bind or staple the sheets on the left.

On your **title block**, you want to have the following information:

a. Your company name, logo, address, phone number, and e-mail address
b. Your job number, your project name and location, including street address, city, and state
c. Revision block: space for you to show the addenda or bulletins that the sheet may have. See Chapter Seven for a detailed discussion on addenda and bulletins.
d. Space for your architectural stamp and architect's signature
e. Space for the sheet title (Floor Plan, Elevations, etc.) and space for the sheet number
f. Copyright notice for your drawings
g. Date: The date that you put on your title block is normally the bid date of the project.

A typical **copyright notice** for your drawings may appear as fine print and include language like:

"Construction documents are original and unpublished materials of the architect. They shall not be copied in any form without the expressed written consent of the architect."

Some offices make it a point of not dating the plans until the plans are ready for bidding. This way they know the plans without a date are preliminary. This creates a problem also: how do you keep track of the plans if they are not dated?

One solution may be to note the date as a "Preliminary Date" before your drawings are ready for bid, and change the date notation to "Bid Date" when your drawings are ready for bid. Some offices also add other spaces to show the various city submittal dates on the title block, i.e., 1st submittal date, 2nd submittal date, 3rd submittal date, etc.

All information that you show on your title block will be Xref into ALL sheets for your construction drawings set. This way, if you revise the information, it will automatically be updated for the entire set.

2. **Organizing the Construction Drawings (CD) Set: Building Construction Drawings Set**

a. **Sheet Index**

There are many ways to organize the construction drawings (CD) set. You want to control how the sheets are numbered and named. One of the most important items is the **Sheet Index**. It is like the table of contents of a book.

The following is a sample sheet index for a building CD set:

Table 5.1   Sample Sheet Index for a Building CD Set

Architectural

A0.0	Title Sheet
GN1.0	Accessibility Requirements
GN2.0	General Notes
AS1.0	Architectural Site Plan
A1.0	Floor Plan
A1.1	Partial Floor Plan (reserved for a large building)
A1.2	Partial Floor Plan (reserved for a large building. Of course, you can add sheets A1.3, A1.4 and so on if necessary.)

A2.0   Reflected Ceiling Plan
A2.1   Partial Reflected Ceiling Plan (reserved for a large building)
A2.2   Partial Reflected Ceiling Plan (reserved for a large building)

A3.0   Roof Plan
A3.1   Partial Roof Plan (reserved for a large building)
A3.2   Partial Roof Plan (reserved for a large building)

A4.0   Exterior Elevations
A5.0   Sections
A6.0   Room, Door, and Window Schedules
A7.0   Details
A8.0   Details
A9.0   Details
A10.0   Hardscape Plans

Structural
ST1.0   General Notes and Details
ST2.0   Framing Details
ST3.0   Framing Details

S1.0   Foundation Plans
S1.1   Partial Foundation Plans (reserved for a large building)
S1.2   Partial Foundation Plans (reserved for a large building)

S2.0   Framing Plans
S2.1   Partial Framing Plans (reserved for a large building)
S2.2   Partial Framing Plans (reserved for a large building)

S3.0   Sections
S3.1   Sections

Electrical
E0.0   Electrical Notes & Details
E0.1   Electrical Notes & Details
E0.2   Electrical Title 24

E1.0   Power Plans & Panel Schedules
E1.1   Partial Power Plans & Panel Schedules (reserved for a large building)
E1.2   Partial Power Plans & Panel Schedules (reserved for a large building)

E2.0   Lighting Plans
E2.1   Partial Lighting Plans (reserved for a large building)
E2.2   Partial Lighting Plans (reserved for a large building)

Mechanical

M0.0	Equipment Schedules, Notes, and Details
M1.0	Mechanical (or HVAC) Floor Plan and T-24 Energy Form
M1.1	Partial Mechanical (or HVAC) Floor Plan and T-24 Energy Form (reserved for a large building)
M1.2	Partial Mechanical (or HVAC) Floor Plan and T-24 Energy Form (reserved for a large building)

Plumbing

P0.0	Plumbing Schedules, Notes, Legend, and Details
P1.0	Plumbing Floor Plans
P1.1	Partial Plumbing Floor Plans (reserved for a large building)
P1.2	Partial Plumbing Floor Plans (reserved for a large building)

b. CD Base Drawings for Consultants

When we work on the construction drawings (CD), we normally prepare the CD base drawings, send the base drawings to our consultants, then the consultants can start their work, and we can further develop the architectural portion of the CD package simultaneously.

The **Building CD Base Drawings for Consultants** normally include <u>floor plans, reflected ceiling plans, roof plans, elevations, and sections</u>. For a retail building, it typically takes 1 or 2 weeks to come up with the CD <u>base</u> drawings for consultants. After the CD base drawings are ready, you will send them to your <u>structural, electrical, mechanical, and plumbing</u> consultants.

If you are also doing the **site development**, you will send your preliminary site plan to the civil engineer, but you want to notify him/her that your plan is <u>for reference ONLY</u>. The civil engineer needs to do field survey and come up with the site plan with <u>accurate</u> dimensions. This is because your preliminary site plan is probably based on hand sketches or some old existing as-built site plan. It probably does NOT have <u>accurate</u> dimensions and is showing your general design intent only.

It probably will take you 2 weeks to complete the first round of CD base drawings. It may take the consultants and you another 2 weeks to complete the first round of <u>uncoordinated</u> CD drawings.

c. The First City Submittal Set

Once your consultants send you their CD drawings, you as an architect will then assemble the complete CD set and then do the first round of review and coordination. You probably want to review and mark up your consultants' drawings first, and then send your markup to your consultants. This is because your consultants need time to update their drawings.

While they are updating their drawings, you can review and mark up the architectural portions of the CD plans and then update them. It will probably take you 1 week to mark up your consultants' drawings and your drawings, and another week for all parties to update the drawings per the markup.

If the project has a tight schedule, you can submit the CD drawing sets to the city as soon as you receive the consultants' drawings and assemble the sets. Then you can do your first round of review and coordination while the city is checking and reviewing your plans. The cities normally take at least 2 weeks to check your plans anyway.

d. Setting up the Construction Drawings Set: What Information Should Go on Each Sheet?

Let us continue to discuss the detailed information for the sheets for the CD package. For floor plans, reflected ceiling plans, roof plans, elevations, and sections, we shall discuss what you will show on CD base drawings, and then what additional information you will show on complete CD set.

Let us discuss what information should go on each sheet:

A0.0   Title Sheet

Checklist for Typical Title Sheet **Content:**

1) Your project name and address (street address, city, and state)
2) Contact information for your client and consultants and your firm
3) Sheet Index (see above)
4) General notes (see discussion below)
5) Vicinity map with the north arrow pointing upwards. You can get it from maps.yahoo.com or draw a simple line drawing with street names.
6) Legend: a few commonly used graphic symbols, such as keynote, building wall section symbol, interior elevation symbol, revision delta, detail reference, exterior material and color symbol, door number, window number, etc.
7) Abbreviations (see detailed discussion in Chapter One)
8) Code analysis (see discussion below)

Optional information that you may want to include on your title sheet:
1) Governing agencies' contact information and name of contact
2) Contact information and name of contact for school fees
3) Contact information and name of contact for dry and wet utility companies: telephone, electricity, gas, water, and sanitation sewer

Using **general notes** properly can be a good way to protect you from professional liabilities. They can be one of your last lines of defense in case of litigation.

A typical **general notes** may include the following. Make sure you review and modify it per your project.

1) All work shall comply with governing codes, regulations, and ordinances.
2) Use dimensions only. Do NOT scale drawings.
3) The general contractor (GC) shall verify all dimensions and field conditions, including but not limited to existing grades, structural framing, landscape features, etc., and report any discrepancies to the architect promptly.
4) GC shall install all portable and permanent fire extinguishers per fire department field inspectors' request and per governing codes.
5) Ventilate the toilet rooms with five air changes per hour.
6) GC shall provide wall or ceiling access panels for electrical, mechanical, plumbing, and fire sprinkler systems per governing codes. Provide a self-closing device in 1-hour rated construction.
7) All penetrations at fire-rated constructions shall be protected by approved fire assemblies.
8) GC shall provide temporary guardrails, pedestrian or vehicular protection barricades, or any other protective devices per governing codes.
9) All exterior studs are 2" x 6" studs at 16" O.C. U.N.O.
10) Exit signs shall be 6" high minimum, with a stroke of ¾" or larger. They shall be worded "EXIT" and shall be installed per governing codes.
11) All exit doors shall be capable of being opened from the inside WITHOUT any special knowledge or effort or the use of a key. Special locking devices shall be approved by the fire department and other governing agencies. Surface bolts or flush bolts shall NOT be used.
12) GC shall provide a durable and readily visible sign stating, "This door must remain unlocked during business hours" on or adjacent to all exit doors. The sign letters shall be 1" or higher and on a contrasting background.
13) Exit doors shall open over a landing not more than ½" below the threshold.
14) Paint all exposed electrical, mechanical, and plumbing equipment, pipes, conduits, etc., with a minimum of two coats of exterior-grade semigloss paint to match adjacent surfaces.
15) GC shall provide and install ALL address and suite numbers per the requirements of the fire department and other governing agencies. Verify required color, (contrasting) background, size, and locations before installation.
16) Before pouring concrete and asphalt paving, GC shall coordinate all conduits and sleeves for irrigation lines under slabs, driveways, sidewalks, etc.

17) GC shall verify with the architect and soils engineer and obtain the complete and latest version of the soils reports, and make them available to all trades as part of the construction documents.

18) GC shall <u>design and build</u> a complete hydraulically calculated automatic fire sprinkler system from the site water main to the interior of the building. GC shall prepare shop drawings and obtain the <u>Insurance Service Office</u> (ISO) approval <u>before</u> submitting them to the architect for approval. GC shall also submit shop drawings to the developer, tenant, and governing agencies for their approval and obtain proper permits before installation.

19) An automatic fire sprinkler system with <u>over 100 heads</u> shall have a local alarm that gives an <u>audible</u> signal at a constantly attended location or is monitored by an approved remote station service or a central location.

20) No <u>hazardous</u> materials shall be stored at the building.

21) GC shall guarantee all work including his subcontractors' work for <u>1</u> year after the final project completion.

22) All materials and equipment shall be installed per <u>manufacturer's recommendations</u> and per industry standards.

23) Contractor and subcontractors shall keep the site <u>free of waste materials and debris</u> caused by their operation. All construction vehicles shall be cleaned properly upon leaving the project site to keep the street free of debris.

24) GC shall be responsible for all temporary utilities.

25) If there are discrepancies or conflicts in the construction documents, the <u>most expensive item</u> shall be considered the item included in the contractor's bid. In this case, the contractor shall contact the architect promptly to get a written interpretation of the <u>design intent</u>.

26) Approval of the component of an assembly shall not be considered as the approval of the entire assembly.

Code Analysis

Code Analysis is difficult for young professionals. Code books have hundreds or even thousands of pages. It is hard to know where to begin.

If you have done it once or twice, it will be much easier for you.

Why?

Because there are only a few code sections that are frequently used. If you have done it once, you will know where to find the information and how to do it.

We are going to use a sample code analysis for a retail building to help you to become familiar with this process. You may be doing other types of building, but there are many **<u>universal</u> requirements** for **ALL** buildings that you can learn from this sample. The codes may be updated in the future, and the code section numbers may change, but **if you can learn from this sample and**

know what you are looking for, you can easily locate the information from the **index** of the new version of the code books in the future.

The following is a sample **code analysis** for a retail building:

Table 5.2   **Sample Code Analysis for a Retail Building**

Applicable Building Codes:

2007 California Building Code (CBC) based on 2006 IBC

2007 California Electrical Code (CEC) based on 2005 NEC

2007 California Mechanical Code (CMC) based on 2006 UMC

2007 California Plumbing Code (CPC) based on 2006 UPC

Energy Code:	California Title 24 Energy
Accessibility Code:	California Title 24 Handicap
Building Zoning:	Commercial
Occupancy Group:	M (Section 309, 2007 CBC)
Number of Stories:	1
Type of Construction:	V-B (Table 601, 2007 CBC), Fully Sprinklered
Building Height:	Main Building 22'-0" < 40'-0" Canopy 26'-0" < 40'-0" (Table 503, 2007 CBC)

Qualification of Building:

Basic Allowable Area: 9,000 s.f. (Table 503, 2007 CBC)

Allowable Area Increase for Fully Sprinklered Building (x4): 36,000 s.f. (Section 506, 2007 CBC)

Actual Building Area = 8,806 s.f. < 36,000 s.f.

If you are doing the building shell only, the code analysis above is probably adequate. If you are also doing tenant improvement work for the building, you probably need to do the following additional code analysis:

Common Path of Egress Travel Distance:

Maximum Travel Distance <u>Allowed</u>: 75 feet for fully sprinklered, M occupancy building (<u>Section 1014</u>, 2007 CBC)

Maximum Travel Distance <u>Provided</u>: 73 feet

Note: You may need to draw a <u>dashed polyline</u> on your floor plan to show the <u>worst-case scenario</u> of your occupants' Common Path of Egress. You can measure the total length of the <u>dashed polyline</u> to get the actual travel distance.

Occupant Load (<u>Table 1004.1.1</u>, 2007 CBC):

Sales Occupancy	5,575 s.f./30 = 186 occupants
Receiving Occupancy	1,893 s.f./300 = 7 occupants
Office Occupancy	<u>1,338 s.f./100 = 14 occupants</u>
Total Occupant Load	207 occupants

(Male: 207/2 = 104, Female = 207/2 = 104)

Minimum Number of Exits

Number of Exits <u>Required</u>: 2 for 500 occupants or less.
(<u>Table 1019.1</u>, 2007 CBC)

Since we have 207 occupants < 500, we need 2 exits.

Number of Exits <u>Provided</u>: 3

Egress Width

All <u>exit</u> doors shall have <u>panic</u> hardware

Egress Width <u>Required</u>: 207 x 0.2 = 41.4" (or 3'-6")
(<u>Table 1005.1</u>, 2007 CBC)

Egress Width <u>Provided</u>: 3' + 3' + 6' = 12' > 3'-6"

Minimum Number of Plumbing Fixtures
(<u>Table 2902.1</u>, 2007 CBC)

(See <u>Occupant Load</u> above)

Toilets (For M Occupancy, 1 per 500 occupants per sex)
Required: Male   1 (104 occupants < 500)   Female   1
Provided: Male   1   Female   1

Lavatories (For M Occupancy, 1 per 750 occupants per sex)
Required: Male   1 (104 occupants < 750)   Female   1
Provided: Male   1   Female   1

Drinking Fountains (For M Occupancy, 1 per 1,000 occupants)
Required: 1 (207 occupants for both sexes < 1,000)
Provided: 1

Other (For M Occupancy, 1 service sink required, 1 service sink provided)

GN1.0   Accessibility Requirements

On Sheet GN1.0, you can list general accessibility requirements as notes or even with a few simple diagrams. Arrange your notes from top to bottom and from left to right. This is different from a detail sheet's layout: you will arrange your details from top to bottom, and from right to left. This is because your sheet's right-hand side will show up first when you open a roll of drawings. It is easier for the contractors to find the details.

We do NOT arrange the notes from right to left because it is too hard to read. This factor outweighs the benefit of finding the notes easily.

Your **general accessibility notes** may include the following aspects:

a.   Site development and path of travel
b.   Walks and sidewalks
c.   Ramps
d.   Curb ramps
e.   Parking
f.   Entrance and exits
g.   Sign and identifications
h.   Electrical accessibility requirements
i.   Floors and levels

Once it is set up, this becomes generic information that you can reuse for many projects. Make sure you read it at least once and review and modify it for your specific project.

GN2.0   General Notes

On Sheet GN2.0, you can list building department, fire department, and health department requirements and plan check correction notes.

These notes can even be copied onto sticky back papers and then pasted on a blank sheet with modified title block information. Once you make a hard copy of this sheet, you can scan it as a pdf file and file it as part of your project's electronic files.

AS1.0   Architectural Reference Site Plan

If you are creating a building CD drawing set, then you can probably save your latest site plan in your site development CD set as a reference site plan for your building CD set.

Checklist for Architectural Reference Site Plan

You want to show the following on sheet AS1.0, Architectural Reference Site Plan:

1) Handicap accessible path of travel from public sidewalks to the accessible entrances and emergency exits of your building. Add a note indicating the slope shall be 5% or less, and the cross slope for sidewalks shall be 2% or less.
2) Use a light-shaded area to indicate the building that you are working on and the adjacent area included as part of the building contract. You can also use a dashed line to enclose this shaded area as "extent of building contract."
3) Building numbers, names, and square footages
4) Property lines
5) Setback line and easements
6) Parcel lines
7) Parking stalls and the numbers of stalls for each row of parking stalls
8) Trash enclosures and trash compactors
9) Monument signs
10) Loading docks
11) Fire truck access paths and major dimensions per fire department. A 25' wide minimum fire truck lane is common. Check with your fire department.
12) Streets, street names, and turning radius
13) Sidewalks
14) Major hardscape features
15) Light poles and transformers and related concrete pads. You can wblock them from your electrical engineer's plans when they are available.
16) Trees and other major landscape features. You can wblock them from your landscape architect's plans when they are available. Check the form, habit,

height, and density of your trees, and <u>make sure they will NOT block the signage of your buildings</u>.

17) Note that <u>signs</u> are shown for reference only, and they are under <u>separate permit</u> and approval.

18) North arrow and scale. A <u>1" = 100'-0"</u> scale is common.

19) Add a note at the bottom of the sheet: "This site plan is for reference only. Site development is a separate CD set under a separate permit and approval."

20) Major **site technical data**, see sample below:

Table 5.3   **Sample Major Site Technical Data**

Land   118 acres (or 5,140,080 s.f.)
Building   1,128,260 s.f.
Coverage   21.95%
Land to Building Ratio   4.56/1

Parking Stalls Required (Per City Requirements):
Retail 886,300 s.f. @ 4/1,000   3,545 stalls
Hotel 160 rooms @ 1/room   160 stalls
Theater 3,284 seats @ ¼ seats   821 stalls
Food Use <u>106,600 s.f @ 10/1,000   1,066 stalls</u>

   Total   5,592 stalls
Standard Parking Size 9' x 19'

Percentage of Compact Parking Stalls Allowed: 20% or 1,118 stalls

Accessible (Handicap) Parking Stalls Required: 66 stalls (<u>Table 11B-6</u>, 2007 CBC)

Including 9 Van-Accessible Parking Stalls per <u>Section 1129B.3</u>, 2007 CBC

Accessible Parking Size: 14' x 19' (Including 5' wide loading area at passenger side)

Van-Accessible Parking Size 17' x 19' (Including 8' wide loading area at the passenger side)

Parking Stalls Provided: 5,592 stalls Including 1,118 compact parking stalls and 66 accessible parking stalls (noted as H.C., 9 of them are van-accessible parking stalls and noted as "Van" on the site plan)

A1.0   Floor Plan

Checklist for Base Floor Plan to S, E, M, and P Engineers

Note: Finish all your base sheets and then <u>send all of them to the engineers at the same time</u>. Do NOT send them one sheet at a time.

You want to show the following items on the base floor plan:

1) Grid lines

   There are a number of ways to label grid lines.

   Some architects simply label the grid lines from left to right with numbers, and from top to bottom with letters.

   The following is my suggestion on setting up the sheet and building grid lines:

   When you set up your Floor Plan Sheet, the typical way is to have your building's main entrance <u>facing the bottom of the sheet</u>. If your sheet cannot accommodate the floor plan, then you can rotate the building and have your building's main entrance facing the <u>right-hand side</u> of the sheet.

   You can label your grid lines <u>from the front of your building to the back of your building as Grid Lines A, B, C</u> …

   Next, imagine that you are standing <u>outside</u>, in front of your building, and <u>facing</u> your building. You can then label the other group of your grid lines <u>from left to right as 1, 2, 3</u> …

   This way, you ALWAYS know where your grid line A is, and where your grid line 1 is.

2) Dimensions: overall dimension string, dimensions between the grids, dimensions defining the shape of the building outlines, dimensions locating interior partitions, and dimensions from outside faces of building exterior walls to property lines.

   Tip for Dimensioning:

   You need 2 horizontal dimensions to locate a building element on the plan. Similarly, the contractor needs 2 horizontal dimensions to locate any architectural elements in the field.

   Think about what dimensions you need to draw the building on a plan, then you know what dimensions you will need to give the contractors so that they can build the building correctly. You do NOT want the contractors to scale your plan for dimensions.

In fact, most of the **requests for information** (RFIs) from the contractors are regarding dimensions. Therefore, if you give the contractors all the dimensions they need on the plans, you will save much more time later during construction in answering phone calls, RFIs, etc.

3) You should dimension to the <u>face</u> of the stud for both wood stud walls and metal stud walls, with one exception: if the stud wall is the **Demising Wall** between two tenants, you should dimension to the <u>centerline</u> of the stud wall.

4) Some tenants want to show the interior dimension as <u>clear</u> dimensions, i.e., a finish-to-finish dimension. They normally have a note indicating that.

5) Scale (⅛" = 1'-0" is typical) and north arrow

6) Show adjacent buildings (if any) as dashed lines.

7) For CMU walls, you should dimension to the <u>face</u> of the CMU.

8) When calculating a **building gross area** or **leasable area**, you should measure to the <u>outside face</u> of the <u>exterior</u> stud or exterior CMU, and measure to the <u>centerline</u> of the <u>interior</u> partition that divides two spaces.

9) Pilasters and canopy columns

10) Structural <u>columns</u>: you may need to send simple sketches back and forth several times to your structural engineer and discuss with him the best locations for the columns.

11) Interior partitions

12) Electrical Room: Coordinate with your electrical engineer. You may need <u>two</u> doors for the electrical room.

13) Coordinate with your electrical engineer and make sure you have enough <u>clearance</u> (3'-0" is typical) in front of the electrical equipment and switchgear. Dimension the clearance space.

14) Toilet rooms and related plumbing fixtures (toilets, sinks, and urinals) with <u>correct fixture counts</u> per codes

15) Janitor's room and mop sink (if required)

16) Roof hatch and roof access ladder

17) Doors and windows with their numbers

18) Check the tenant's criteria and check with your mechanical engineer to find out if you need to use ¼" <u>glazing</u> or 1" <u>insulated</u> glazing for the exterior windows and storefront.

19) Room names and numbers

Note: When you number the rooms, make sure you number them in an orderly sequence.

I suggest you number them <u>clockwise and continuously</u>. Do <u>NOT</u> jump back and forth. This will make it so much easier for the contractor to read the plans and make it so much easier for people to locate the rooms after the building is built.

You can also consider the <u>building level</u> when you number the rooms. For example, for rooms on the first floor, you can number them as room 101, 102, 103, etc. For rooms on the second floor, you can number them as room 201, 202, 203, etc.

If you have rooms on <u>both sides</u> of a corridor (like a hotel or condominium), you need to number the rooms on one side as <u>odd</u> numbers and rooms on the other side as <u>even</u> numbers. Again, this is to make it easier for people to locate the rooms.

It is customary to number **addresses** on the <u>north</u> side of a **street** as <u>odd</u> numbers, addresses on the <u>south</u> side of a street as <u>even</u> numbers, addresses on the <u>west</u> side of a street as <u>odd</u> numbers, and addresses on the <u>east</u> side of a street as <u>even</u> numbers.

Mnemonics: For a typical map, north is on <u>top</u>, south is on the bottom, west is on the <u>left</u>, and east is on the right. When we read, we read from left to right, and from top to bottom. When we count, we count from <u>odd</u> numbers to even numbers (1, 2, 3 ...). Therefore, <u>north</u> is related to <u>odd</u> number since it is on <u>top</u>, <u>west</u> is related to <u>odd</u> number since it is on the <u>left</u>.

Similarly, you can number **rooms** on the <u>north</u> side of a **corridor** as <u>odd</u> numbers, rooms on the <u>south</u> side of a corridor as <u>even</u> numbers, rooms on the <u>west</u> side of a corridor as <u>odd</u> numbers, and rooms on the <u>east</u> side of a corridor as <u>even</u> numbers.

You can also <u>relate the door and/or window numbers to your room number</u>. For example, you can number the door at room 101 as door number 101 also. If you have two doors for room 101, you can number them as door 101a and door 101b. The <u>graphic</u> symbols for room numbers, door numbers, and window numbers should be <u>different</u> so that people will not be confused.

20) Parking stalls, sidewalks, ramps, and curb ramps around the building
21) Trash enclosures next to the building
22) Spot finish surface (<u>F.S.</u>) <u>elevations</u> around the building at every corner of exterior building walls and every exit or entrance
23) If you are using <u>thresholds</u>, you can have the spot <u>F.S. elevations</u> at exterior doors to <u>match</u> your building's finish floor elevation. If you are <u>NOT</u> using thresholds, you can have the spot <u>F.S. elevations</u> at exterior doors to be ¼" <u>below</u> your building's finish floor elevation. This is because of the handicap codes requirements.

Note: F.S. elevations are typically noted in feet, such as 20.00', 19.96', 21.50', etc.

24) Spot <u>F.S. elevations</u> for loading docks. Please check your tenant's criteria for loading dock depth. These are common depths: <u>4'-0"</u> or <u>3'-10"</u>.

25) Make sure that you note the <u>1.5% slope away</u> from the building for the concrete or AC paving finish surfaces around your buildings. You want the water to <u>drain away</u> from your building. Landscape areas that people will not walk on can have a steeper slope, but should still be less than <u>2:1</u> slope; otherwise, you may need to use retaining walls.

Note: A <u>2:1</u> slope is a slope where the ratio of the horizontal dimension to vertical dimension is 2:1.

26) Trench drain and related connection to site storm drain at the bottom of loading docks. The trench drain is typically <u>NOT</u> placed at the very end of the loading dock, but about <u>3'-0"</u> from its end.

27) CMU walls or guardrails around the loading docks. Check with the city to find out if the loading dock needs to be screened with a CMU wall. If the answer is "yes," the CMU wall around the loading dock may need to be <u>6'-0"</u> to <u>8'-0"</u> high. Otherwise, it can be a CMU wall or guardrail at <u>3'-6"</u> height above the highest adjacent grades.

28) Top of wall (T.O.W.) elevations for CMU wall

29) Overhead door for the loading dock entrance: Is it a coiling door or a panelized door? If it is a <u>panelized door</u>, then coordinate with your structural engineer to make sure the structural braces and other members <u>will not interfere with</u> the <u>track</u> of the panelized door.

30) Top of curb (T.O.C.) spot elevations

31) Switch gear and related concrete pad, transformer and related concrete pad, sewer, waterlines, gas line, gas meters, automatic sprinkler risers, roof drain leaders, overflow drain leaders, etc. You may need to send simple sketches back and forth several times to your engineers and discuss with them the best locations for these items. Verify their sizes with your engineers.

32) Coordinate with your civil and plumbing engineers: if storm drains are near your building, confirm with the owner and then <u>tie your **roof drain**</u> to the <u>storm drain</u>; if not, run your roof drain lines under the sidewalks and <u>spill them at the curb</u> <u>faces</u>.

33) Do <u>NOT</u> tie **<u>overflow</u>** drain lines to storm drains. Spill overflow drains at 8" AFF and at <u>noticeable</u> locations.

34) Landscape planters and areas around the building

35) Any other important information that you want your engineers to know

Additional Checklist for a City Submittal Floor Plan

After you send out your base sheet package to your consultants, you can continue to work and add the following items:

1) Floor plan notes and detailed keynotes
2) Review and coordinate keynotes with graphic symbols on the plan.

3) Coordinate with other sheets and add all detail references/call-outs.
4) Pipe guards/bollards for gas meters, electrical transformers, switchgears, trash enclosures, building corners, etc., if they are exposed to vehicle traffic.
5) Bike racks
6) Show fire-rated walls with special graphic symbols
7) Handrails and guardrails
8) Coat hooks
9) Note toilet room accessories
10) Add detailed dimensions to toilet rooms, hallways, etc., to meet handicap codes.
11) Tactile egress sign locations
12) Roof drain downspouts and splash blocks
13) Coordinate with your structural engineer and shade in your shear walls.
14) For wood stud buildings, use 6" high concrete curbs at bases of all exterior walls, if possible, except at retail building exterior walls where you think they may change to storefront or exits/entrances in the future.
15) For wood stud buildings, all exterior walls along the seismic gap shall be 1-hour rated.
16) If your building is higher than adjacent buildings, you should use below-grade waterproofing.
17) At areas visible to the public, use furred walls to hide utility lines at exterior CMU walls.
18) Your furred walls shall have expansion joints where your exterior CMU wall expansion joints occur.
19) The top of curb ramp shall have 4' x 4' clear space
20) Coordinate with your structural engineer and show expansion joints for CMU walls.

A2.0 Reflected Ceiling Plan

Checklist for a Base Reflected Ceiling Plan to S, E, M, and P Engineers

Note: Finish all your base sheets and then send all of them to the engineers at the same time. Do NOT send them one sheet at a time.

You want to show the following items on the base floor plan:

1) Grid lines
2) Scale (⅛" = 1'-0" is typical) and north arrow
3) Show adjacent buildings (if any) as dashed lines.
4) Ceiling plan legend
5) Room names and numbers
6) Door and window headers
7) Ceiling finishes: T-bar ceilings, gypsum board ceiling, plaster ceiling, etc.

8) Coordinate with your electrical engineer and show light fixtures at proper spacing, including 2 x 4 recess lights, track lights, down lights and <u>wall-mounted lights</u> on exterior columns, pilasters, and walls. If you do <u>NOT</u> show these wall-mounted lights, <u>your electrical engineer will very likely miss them</u> on their plans. This is based on experience.
9) Do NOT miss the lights under the canopy. Place them at roughly <u>12'-0"</u> O.C.
10) Dimensions to locate light fixtures
11) Canopy access hatches/panels
12) Canopy and exterior soffit vents
13) Show fabric awnings and metal canopy as solid lines, NOT dashed lines.
14) Any other important information that you want your engineers to know

Additional Checklist for a City Submittal Reflected Ceiling Plan

After you send out your base sheet package to your consultants, you can continue to work and add the following items:

1) Ceiling plan notes and detailed keynotes
2) Review and coordinate keynotes with graphic symbols on the plan.
3) Coordinate with other sheets and add all detail references/call-outs.
4) Show control joints at 10'-0" O.C. maximum for gypsum board ceiling and plaster ceiling.
5) Coordinate with exterior elevations and show material colors and finish for exterior soffits and canopy ceiling.
6) Coordinate with your mechanical engineer, and add HVAC supply and return <u>registers</u> and <u>exhaust fans</u> on ceiling plans. You can simply get an electronic file from your mechanical engineer and wblock the information, but you need to coordinate their locations and <u>make sure there is NO overlapping</u> or conflict with electrical lights or other items. Electrical, mechanical, and plumbing (EMP) plans are normally <u>diagrammatic</u> and do NOT show the exact locations. You as an architect determine the final and exact location of the lights, registers, and exhaust fans.
7) Closure strip detail references at gaps with adjacent buildings

A3.0   Roof Plan

Checklist for Base Roof Plan to S, E, M, and P Engineers

Note: *Finish all your base sheets and then <u>send all of them to the engineers at the same time</u>. Do NOT send them one sheet at a time.*

You want to show the following items on the base roof plan:

1) Grid lines
2) Scale (⅛" = 1'-0" is typical) and north arrow

3) Show adjacent buildings (if any) as dashed lines.
4) Roof plan legend
5) Building section symbols and wall section symbols
6) Parapet braces and related access doors and vents

Note: You can probably only have about 5'-0" of <u>unbraced</u> wood stud parapet and maybe 6'-0" to 8'-0" of <u>unbraced</u> reinforced CMU parapet. If the parapet is higher, you probably need to add braces.

Coordinate with your structural engineer regarding the maximum unbraced parapet heights for your building.

7) Vents and access doors for enclosed canopy towers per codes
8) Minimum two roof drains and two overflow drains. Coordinate with the plumbing engineer for the exact number needed. Locate them between structural members.
9) The inlet of an overflow drain should be 2" higher than that of the adjacent roof drain.
10) Top of Sheathing (T.O.S.) elevations at every structural column and building corner

Note: When deciding the <u>T.O.S. elevations</u>, use ¼" per foot minimum slope and make sure you have enough space to accommodate the structural members (roof deck beams and joists/trusses), mechanical ductwork, and ceiling assembly with lights.

A simple rule of thumb is to keep at least 18" clearance between the bottom of the lowest roof joists/trusses and the ceiling assembly. Pay attention to the direction of the roof joists/trusses and mechanical ductwork also. Sometimes you can run the ductwork parallel to roof joists/trusses and between them.

11) Top of Parapet (T.O.P.) elevations at every building corner

Note: Make sure rooftop mechanical/HVAC units are screened by the parapet walls when setting the <u>T.O.P. elevations</u>. You may need to do a simple sectional view line study. You can use 5'-6" as a normal person's eye level when you do the study.

Some cities may require the <u>T.O.P. elevations</u> to be set at the same height or higher than the top of the rooftop HVAC units.

12) Minimum <u>30"</u> parapet height at protected exterior wall and at the property line along adjacent buildings (Section <u>704.11.1</u>, 2006 IBC)
13) Roof access hatch and roof walking pad

14) Make sure you show a standard roof hatch safety railing. It can be a simple note calling out the manufacturer and model number and a simple graphic on your roof hatch detail.
15) Coordinate with your mechanical engineer and show the rooftop HVAC units. Maintain at least 3'-0" clearance space around the HVAC units. Some cities may have a minimum distance requirement from the HVAC to the roof edge.
16) Roof crickets at the high side of HVAC units and hard to drain corners
17) General direction of the drainage with the slope at ¼" per foot
18) Show and note roof ridgelines.
19) Show and reference draft stops per codes.

Additional Checklist for City Submittal Roof Plan

After you send out your base sheet package to your consultants, you can continue to work and add the following items:

1) Review and coordinate keynotes with graphic symbols on the plan.
2) Coordinate with other sheets and add all detail references/call-outs.
3) Show detailed dimensions to locate all important roof structural elements, like lengths of parapet walls and their extensions onto the roof
4) Reference flashing details for gaps between buildings
5) Roof plan notes and detailed keynotes

Typical Roof Plan Notes may include the following:

1) Confirm all roof areas have positive drainage before installing the roof sheathing.
2) All elevations are measured from the building finish floor.
3) Verify all roof openings and penetrations with related subcontractors.
4) Provide proper flashing for all utilities line penetrations and vent pipes.
5) Use "Class-A" roofing.
6) Provide reflective and light color cap sheets for all roofing. Verify color with the architect.
7) All HVAC units shall be placed on factory curbs.
8) Install dormer vents at 20'-0" for parapet braces.
9) At toe of parapet braces, provide 2x blocking between trusses.
10) Paint all exposed rooftop conduits, pipes & other accessories with two coats of exterior-grade semigloss paint to match the roof surface.

A4.0   Exterior Elevations

Checklist for Base Exterior Elevations Sheet to S, E, M, and P Engineers

Note: Finish all your base sheets and then send all of them to the engineers at the same time. Do NOT send them one sheet at a time.

You want to show the following items on the base Exterior Elevations Sheet:

1) Grid lines: Check grid line numbers against the floor plan.
2) Scale (⅛" = 1'-0" is typical)
3) Show adjacent buildings (if any) as dashed lines. Add the name of adjacent buildings.
4) Building section, wall section, and canopy section symbols
5) Major (mostly vertical) dimensions defining the shape of the building outlines, like top of parapet, bottom of soffits, top of storefront, etc. You should dimension to the Finish Floor (FF).
6) Adjust the exterior finish line per actual grades around the building.
7) Major materials call-outs
8) Show roof tiles as a half-tonc hatch pattern.

Additional Checklist for Elevations Sheet in City Submittal Set

After you send out your base sheet package to your consultants, you can continue to work and add the following items:

1) Review and coordinate keynotes with graphic symbols on the plan.
2) Coordinate with other sheets and add all detail references/call-outs.
3) Show detailed dimensions to locate ALL exterior features, like top of doors and windows, major reveal lines, control joints, signage areas, fabric awning, etc.
4) Reference closure strip at gaps between the buildings
5) Dashed in roof sheathing lines behind the parapet
6) Dashed in canopy soffit lines
7) Show finish floor elevations, especially when they are different from those of adjacent buildings.
8) Exterior roof access ladder (if any). Lower parapet at ladder locations to less than 18'-0" to avoid an intermediate landing.
9) Show roof overflow drain outlets and exterior roof drain downspouts (if any).
10) Exterior light fixtures (both decorative and security lights) at ALL elevations. Coordinate with the electrical engineer for mounting heights.
11) Masonry wall expansion joints (typically at 20'-0" O.C. max.). Coordinate with the structural engineer regarding joint spacing. If plaster is applied over masonry, plaster joints (typically at 10'-0" O.C. max.) shall also occur at every masonry joint location.
12) Do NOT show door swing symbols because they do NOT give the contractor any additional information (the floor plan already shows the door swing directions), and they have to be updated every time a door swing direction is changed.
13) Dash in electrical equipment and show the related concrete curbs as solid lines.

14) Dash in rooftop mechanical/HVAC units <u>ONLY</u> if required by the city's plan check.

Why?

Because some rooftop mechanical/HVAC units may be <u>higher</u> than the top of the parapet, but they <u>cannot be seen</u> if you do a view line study because of their distance to the edge of the building.

If you dash them in, then they may appear higher than the top of the parapet and the city may ask you to raise your parapet height. Then, you may have to do a <u>full-blown and attractive</u> view line analysis to convince the city again.

Why do you want these troubles?

As long as you do a simple view line study yourself and know they are not visible, it is fine. Do NOT waste your time and effort to do a <u>full-blown and attractive</u> view line analysis unless you have to.

15) Exterior fire sprinkler riser (if any)
16) Complete materials and colors call-outs. Every surface of the exterior MUST have <u>both</u> materials and colors call-outs.

*Note: You can use **letter** for <u>materials</u> and **numbers** for <u>colors</u> for your materials and colors call-outs. This is because you will probably have more colors than types of materials, and we have 26 letters and 99 single-digit or double-digit numbers.*

You can go to any of the major manufacturers' websites to get a <u>color palette and many material choices</u>. See Chapter One for manufacturers' websites information. Once you have the information from their websites, you can select materials and colors to closely <u>match</u> the color design elevations or rendering of your project.

Materials and colors call-outs are <u>difficult</u> for young professionals.
Here is a sample to show you how much information to show on the call-outs:

Table 5.4   **Sample Materials and Colors Call-outs**

MATERIALS:
A/-	8" x 8" x 16" SPLIT FACE CONCRETE BLOCK (CMU)
B/-	8" x 8" x 16" PRECISION CONCRETE BLOCK (CMU)
C/-	CONCRETE SIDEWALK
D/-	FULL BRICK BY <u>PACIFIC CLAY BLOCK</u>

Note: You can specify a local manufacturer that is close to your project site. Typ.

F/-   THIN BRICK VENEER BY <u>PACIFIC CLAY BLOCK</u>
G/-   ALUMINUM BREAK METAL
H/-   ALUMINUM STOREFRONT WITH 1" INSULATED CLEAR GLAZING. INSTALL SAFETY AND TEMPERED GLAZING PER LOCAL CODES.
I/-   METAL AWNING WITH CONCEALED SEAM
J/-   STANDING SEAM METAL ROOF BY <u>AEP SPAN</u>
K/-   16" WIDE METAL BAND
L/-   EXTERIOR PLASTER WITH <u>FINE SAND FLOAT</u> FINISH AND ELASTOMERIC COATING

Note: You can call out other finishes for plaster for your project, such as <u>SANTA BARBARA</u> FINISH, <u>MEDIUM SAND FLOAT FINISH</u>, etc.

M/   LIGHT FIXTURE. SEE ELECTRICAL DRAWINGS FOR MORE INFORMATION.
N/-   ELECTRICAL SWITCH GEAR. SEE ELECTRICAL DRAWINGS FOR MORE INFORMATION.

COLORS:
-/1   "PLUM" BY <u>ANGELUS BLOCK</u>

Note: You can specify a local manufacturer that is close to your project site. Typ.

-/2   "WARM GREY" BY <u>ANGELUS BLOCK</u>
-/3   SP 100 "CHATEAU" BY DUNN EDWARDS (DE)
-/4   DE 3024 "SOLID GRANITE" BY DE
-/5   SP 101 "TOPAZ" BY DE
-/6   309 "ROW HOUSE" BY ICI
-/7   DARK BROWN ANODIZED ALUMINUM FINISH
-/8   "SUNSET RED" BY PACIFIC CLAY
-/9   NATURAL COLOR
-/10   PRIME AND PAINT TO MATCH ADJACENT SURFACE

So

A/1 refers to "PLUM" COLOR 8" x 8" x 16" SPLIT FACE CONCRETE BLOCK (CMU) BY <u>ANGELUS BLOCK</u>.

C/9 refers to NATURAL COLOR CONCRETE SIDEWALK.

You can call out other materials and colors in a similar manner.

17) Complete Elevation Notes

The following is a **sample Elevation Notes**:

a) GC shall <u>verify</u> all exterior finishes, colors, and materials with the architect. GC shall notify the architect of any <u>discrepancies</u> and obtain the architect's written clarification of <u>design intent</u> BEFORE proceeding.

b) Coordinate with the sign contractor and provide 2x continuous <u>blocking</u> in the stud wall for signage attachments.

c) Apply ⅞" thick cement plaster over lath and moisture barrier over a minimum ½" thick exterior-grade plywood over exterior-grade studs, and ⅝" thick cement plaster over CMU walls where the plaster finish is called out. Typ.

d) Split face CMU walls shall <u>NOT</u> have a plaster finish.

e) Construction joints of the EPS foam cornice shall be at <u>20'-0"</u> O.C. maximum.

f) Wrap metal reveals <u>around</u> pilasters and columns.

g) <u>Back</u> of parapets shall have exterior finishes.

h) Continue the finish along the <u>sides and back</u> of exterior columns and along the <u>sides</u> of pilaster/building pop-outs. Typ.

i) Paint all <u>exposed</u> metal flashing and building accessories, pipes, conduits, equipment, etc., to match adjacent surface. Typ.

j) All bricks shall have <u>rake</u> joints.

   Note: You can call out the type of joints you prefer.

k) Exterior finish grades shown on exterior elevations are diagrammatic. See floor plans and civil plans for more information on exterior grades.

A5.0   Sections

Checklist for Base Section Sheet to S, E, M, and P Engineers

Note: Finish all your base sheets and then <u>send all of them to the engineers at the same time</u>. Do NOT send them one sheet at a time.

You want to show the following items on the base Exterior Elevations Sheet:

1) Grid lines: check grid line numbers against the floor plan.
2) Scale: ⅜" = 1'-0" is typical.
3) Adjacent buildings (if any) as dashed lines. Show the names of adjacent buildings.
4) Organize the sections from <u>top to bottom</u> and from <u>right to left</u> on your sheet. This is because when you open a roll of construction drawings, the <u>right-hand</u> side of the sheet will show up first.
5) <u>Major</u> (mostly vertical) <u>dimensions</u> defining the <u>shape</u> of the building outlines, like the top of the parapet, the bottom of soffits, the top of storefronts, etc. You should dimension to the finish floor (FF).
6) Adjust the exterior finish line per actual <u>grades</u> around the building.
7) Major materials call-outs
8) Show roof tiles as a half-tone hatch pattern
9) 6" high concrete curbs (if any) at the bottom of wood or metal stud walls
10) Do <u>NOT</u> show <u>structural</u> members <u>except</u> the most basic framing <u>outline</u>, like 2x stud walls, CMU walls, etc. Just show your <u>section profile</u>, i.e., outline of the wall sections, top of the roof, bottom of ceilings and soffits, and some diagrammatic framing information to show the type of construction (wood studs, metal studs, CMU, etc.) for your building.
11) Coordinate with the roof plan to make sure <u>roof sheathing heights</u> are shown correctly on sections <u>graphically</u>. This is <u>VERY</u> important because it may affect the structural connection design.
12) All "Not in Contract" (NIC) items such as tenant signage shall be shown as dashed lines.

Additional Checklist for Section Sheet in City Submittal Set

After you send out your base sheet package to your consultants, you can continue to work and add the following items:

1) Review and <u>coordinate keynotes</u> with graphic symbols on sections.
2) <u>Detailed</u> dimensions to locate ALL exterior features, like the top of doors and windows, major reveal lines, control joints, signage areas, fabric awning, etc.
3) Coordinate with other sheets, and add comprehensive keynotes and detail references/call-outs to <u>one main section</u> (for example, Section 1/A5.0). For other sections, just add <u>unique</u> keynotes and detail references/call-outs for these sections, and then add a note: "Refer to Section 1/A5.0 for typical information not shown."

The following is a **sample Keynotes** to show you how much information you need to give the contractor:

Table 5.5   **Sample Section Keynotes**

Note: The graphic symbols for numbers of keynotes shall be different from those of general notes to avoid confusion.

<1>   Plaster over ½" thick plywood over stud framing. See elevation for color and finish.

<2>   See structural drawings for framing.

<3>   Ceiling. See the ceiling plan.

<4>   Light fixture. See the electrical drawings.

<5>   Finish floor

<6>   Concrete curb

<7>   "J" box for "Not in Contract" (NIC) tenant sign

<8>   Dark bronze aluminum storefront with 1" insulated clear glazing. Use safety and tempered glazing at locations required by codes.

<9>   Brace vents. See roof plan for locations and detail sheet for more information.

<10> 3'-0" wide, ⅝" thick plywood catwalk for the entire length of the canopy.

<11> NIC tenant sign. The contractor to provide blocking for the sign.

<12> Parapet braces. See structural drawings for more information. Provide blocking (beneath roof sheathing) at toe of braces. Typical.

<13> Use R-19 Batt insulation for exterior walls, and R-22 rigid insulation over roof sheathing. Typical for the entire building.

<14> Drip Edge

<15> Access panel. See roof plan for the location.

<16> 4" continuous soffit vents for the entire length of the canopy. See detail sheet for more information.

<17> Caulk and seal to maintain a watertight condition.

<18> ½" gyp board enclosed space draft stop per codes

<19> Brick veneer anchored to ½" thick plywood (with wall ties) over the stud framing. Install per manufacturer's recommendation. See the detail sheet for more information.

<20> Canopy soffit access panel. See the detail sheet for more information.

4) Add Section Notes.

The following is a sample **Section Notes**:

a) Framing and structural members shown in architectural plans are generic and diagrammatic. See structural plans for accurate information and exact sizes and locations.

b) Provide draft stop at concealed attic space or mansard roof at 100 linear feet O.C. max., and per codes.

c) Continue the finish along the sides and back of exterior columns and along the sides of pilaster/building pop-outs. Typ.

d) For metal construction, i.e., metal canopy and so on: weld all around and grind smooth all connections, shop prime all steel, prime all field weld. Paint all steel with two coats of enamel paint. See colors schedule on the elevation sheet for colors.

5) All NIC items such as tenant signage shall be shown as dashed lines.

6) Coordinate with your structural drawings to make sure you provide access to tenant signage, especially its "J" box. You may need to cut a 2' wide x 3' high opening at a structural shear wall to provide access.

A6.0   Room, Door, and Window Schedules

Checklist for Schedules Sheet in City Submittal Set

On this sheet, you can show the following items:

1) Room Finish Schedule. It is basically an excel sheet style table, including room numbers, floor finish, wall finish and base, ceiling finish, detail reference (if any), and interior finish notes.

2) Door Schedule. It is basically an excel sheet style table, including door numbers, door type and the related graphics of various types of doors, manufacturer and model number, quantity, thickness, door material, frame materials, remarks, detail reference (if any), and door schedule general notes.

3) Window Schedule. It is basically an excel sheet style table, including window numbers, window type and the related graphics of various types of windows, manufacturer and model number, quantity, thickness, frame materials, remarks, detail reference (if any), and window schedule general notes.

4) Make sure you coordinate all the items on these schedules with the floor plan or floor finish plan, and make sure they match.

Believe me, many times when I do quality control of CD, I have found rooms listed on the room schedule but NOT on the floor plan, and vice versa.

So check each item room by room, door by door, and window by window. It is tedious but important.

5) Make sure the floor finish, wall finish, and wall base of your restrooms, janitor's room, and food prep areas meet health department requirements if your client or tenant sells foods in your building, including prepackaged foods like candies.

A7.0   Details

After you put in the title block, a typical 30 x 42 sheet can be divided into 5 rows and 6 columns, so you can place 30 (5 x 6 = 30) details on one sheet. You should number the details from <u>top to bottom</u> and <u>from right to left</u>.

You should try to <u>group all the similar details together</u>. For example, you can group all the roof details as one sheet, other exterior details as one sheet, storefront and interior details as one sheet, etc.

Within the same sheet, you should also organize the details in a logical manner. For example, you can arrange the top of parapet, bottom of parapet, wall base, and footing details from top to bottom.

You can read books or go to various manufacturers' websites to come up with the typical detail sheets for your office.

Just be careful:

Manufacturers will give you details for "free." They have expertise and they do give you valuable information on how to put the pieces together, but they are also in the business to sell their products. They have good incentives to specify their own products in their details and specifications. Of course, you can use their products, but sometimes these may not be the best solutions for your projects. You need to exercise your own professional judgment.

Once you set up your typical details sheets, you can then review, revise, and reuse them repeatedly for your projects, and then you have a good chance to turn your architectural practice into a profitable and successful business.

Let us use sheet A7.0 as an exterior detail sheet.

Again, the most important tip for quality control of a project is "**Don't leak and don't fall.**" For the "don't fall" part, you need to pick a good structural engineer, and you need to do a good job to coordinate with him. For the "**Don't leak**" part, you need to make sure <u>ALL</u> your exterior details need to work and <u>keep the water and moisture out of your building</u>.

Here are some tips for developing the exterior details:

1) For top of parapet details, you want to use <u>shaped</u> 2x nailers on top for both wood stud construction and CMU walls.

   You want to <u>slope</u> the top of the parapet from front to back of the parapet at a <u>2%</u> slope so that most of the water will drain toward the <u>back</u> of the parapet. This way, you will likely not have the <u>unsightly watermark</u> on the front of your parapet. However, you want to still use a drip edge on the front in case some water does find its way to the front.

Make sure you add a note to prime and paint the front of the parapet coping and drip edge to either match the adjacent surface or per the color of your design elevations and rendering, as specified on the materials and color schedule of your exterior elevation sheet.

There are two common ways to cover the top of the parapet: sheet metal coping or single-ply roofing with a drip edge on the front. The single-ply method is extremely helpful and may be the ONLY way to detail this condition when you have a wide and relatively flat parapet.

Do NOT use plaster on top of the parapet. It is very hard to make it look neat and clean. It is also hard to keep water from getting inside the walls.

For the back of the parapet, you can use plaster finish, shingle finish, or single-ply roofing. If you are using single-ply roofing, the way to detail is to run the single-ply roofing all the way up to the top of the parapet, and then over and connect to the front drip edge with fasteners @ 6" O.C. Go to **Johns Manville** or similar manufacturers' websites and you can find all kinds of details (maybe even in AutoCAD format) for this condition.

2) For the bottom of the parapet, if you are using plaster finish or shingle finish, you need to use flashing and counterflashing. You can go to **Fry Reglet** or similar manufacturers' websites and find all kinds of details (maybe even in AutoCAD format) for this condition.

   If you are using single-ply roofing, then the connection between the roofing pieces will be mechanical fasteners and hot weld. Go to **Johns Manville** or similar manufacturers' websites and find all kinds of details (maybe even in AutoCAD format) for this condition.

3) For the roof hatch, you can go to **Bilco** or similar manufacturers' websites and find a typical detail. It can be a good base for you to develop your own detail. In addition to the typical flashing and counterflashing for the roof hatch curb, make sure you specify a safety post extension for the roof access ladder and the standard roof hatch safety railing.

   ***Note: Roof hatch safety railing** IS required by both OSHA Standards 29 CFR 1910.23 and 29 CFR 1910.27.*

   I know at least three manufacturers who make them. See the links below:
   www.simplifiedbuilding.com/keehatch.php
   www.freepatentsonline.com/6681528.html
   www.4specs.com/s/07/07-7230.html

4) For roof vent and roof access panel details, make sure you specify <u>continuous sealer</u> around the vent or panel frame to maintain a watertight condition and <u>G.I. Drip</u> on top of the opening.

5) Plaster shall terminate at <u>casing beads</u>. Typ.

6) All roof penetration details should have proper **flashing** or membrane boot with a minimum height per codes and industry standard (<u>6" or 8"</u> minimum is typical).

7) Make sure you specify proper **weep screed** for plaster at the base of the exterior walls. The weep screed shall be at least 2" above the adjacent exterior surface. This is to keep moisture from getting into the walls.

8) All wood stud construction shall be properly detailed so that <u>wood</u> members will be at least <u>2 or 3 inches above</u> exterior adjacent grades. Keep wood away from <u>wet</u> surfaces, water, and potential moisture.

9) Make sure you detail the extension for stair handrails (<u>12" at top and 12" plus the width of one thread at the bottom</u>) and ramp handrails (<u>12" top and bottom</u>).

10) For **guardrails**, the top is <u>3'-6"</u> high. A <u>4" ball</u> shall not be able to pass through the gaps between guardrail members. For **handrails**, the top of the railing is <u>2'-10"</u> above the nose of the stair steps or ramp surface. Make sure you properly detail the transaction between the two.

11) Overflow downspout outlets shall be at least <u>8"</u> above adjacent exterior surfaces.

A8.0 Details

This can also be an exterior detail sheet.

A9.0 Details

This can be a storefront and interior detail sheet. You can start by going to **Kawneer** or similar manufacturers' websites and find many typical storefront details.

You then need to add information regarding the <u>connection between</u> the storefront and walls, storefront and columns to the detail. A typical way is to use <u>sealant over backer rod over ¼"</u> **shim**.

Exposed steel columns next to a storefront frame shall be wrapped with <u>aluminum</u> **break metal** to create a better look and finish to match the storefront frame. For wide-flange columns, you may need to place plywood over 2x members to box the "gaps" at the wide-flange columns to create flat surfaces as supports for the aluminum break metal.

Make sure you check the energy calculations and tenant's criteria, and check with your mechanical engineer to find out if you need to use <u>1" insulated glazing</u>. You need to be <u>consistent</u> on your glazing call-outs for the elevations, sections, and details. Make sure you update the <u>graphic</u> symbols for the storefront details if you are using <u>1"</u> insulated glazing instead of <u>¼"</u> glazing.

For interior details and enlarged plans, ALWAYS put in all the required <u>clearances</u> and <u>dimensions</u> at restrooms (both for the enlarged plans and interior elevations for plumbing fixtures) and at workstations per handicap codes. City's plan checkers always look for these <u>clearances</u> and <u>dimensions</u>.

ADA diagrams, *Title 24, California Disabled Accessibility Guidebook* (**CalDAG**) & *California Accessibility Reference Manual Code & Checklist* (**CARM**) will be very helpful for you to put in these dimensions.

For T-bar ceiling details, make sure you call out <u>diagonal braces</u> and <u>compression strut</u> for California jobs. These are for the <u>seismic</u> requirements in California.

Has structural support been shown for water heaters on plumbing sheets? If not, you need to coordinate with plumbing plans and add it to the architectural detail sheet.

A10.0   Hardscape Plans

You want to show the following items on the hardscape plan:

1) Grid lines
2) Scale (⅛" = 1'-0" is typical) and north arrow
3) Show adjacent buildings (if any) as dashed lines.
4) Make sure you call out all <u>expansion joints</u> and <u>tooled joints</u>, as well as <u>color</u> and <u>texture</u> for your concrete finish area, like exterior patio, sidewalks, etc.

What is the difference between **expansion joints** (or **construction joints**) and **tooled joints** (or **control joints**)?

Expansion joints are joints that <u>COMPLETELY</u> separate two (2) pieces of concrete slabs or sidewalks, while the depth of **tooled joints** is only about ¼ of the thickness of the concrete. It comes out to be about ¾" to 1" deep.

Expansion joints shall be placed at 20'-0" O.C. max., while **tooled joints** shall be placed at 6'-0" O.C. max.

Try to align your expansion joints with the corners of your building, pilasters, and columns, and then place tooled joints evenly between expansion joints, i.e., the centerline of two (2) expansion joints, etc.

5) Make sure that you note the 1.5% slope away from the building for your concrete or AC paving surface around the buildings. You want the water to drain away from your building.

3. Coordination of Construction Drawings

After you receive all your consultants' drawings and compile a complete CD set, you can start to coordinate your drawings.

You can start by reviewing and coordinating your consultants' drawings first, and then reviewing and coordinating the architectural sheets.

The easiest way to do it is to use a highlighter and highlight each detail, enlarged plan, elevation, and section when it is referenced. This way, any detail, enlarged plan, elevation, and section that are not highlighted are NOT referenced in the set yet. You need to revise the sheets and add references for them.

At least read the complete CD set line-by-line and word-for-word once. You can find so many errors by simply reading the entire set from beginning to end. You can also highlight the important information as you go.

a. Coordination of Structural Drawings

ST1.0   General Notes and Details

Checklist:

1) The structural engineer often refers to the soils report in the General Notes on this sheet. Check and make sure the correct title, company name, date, and latest version of the soils report are noted on this sheet.
2) The proper type of concrete is specified per the soils report and the tenant's criteria, i.e., 3,000 psi or 3,500 psi, etc.
3) If the concrete is over 2,500 psi, then special inspection is probably required. Make sure it is properly noted. If the structural design does NOT require the concrete to be over 2,500 psi, but you have to use it because of the tenant's criteria, you should add a note like "3,000 psi concrete is NOT required by design. It is used for better quality per criteria only. Special inspection is NOT required."

4) The bottom of the footing for the adjacent building shall be at about the same elevation to <u>avoid discharge</u> from the footing of the higher building.

5) Check and make sure the proper <u>footing width and depth and proper</u> **Grade Beams** are specified and detailed per the soils report and the tenant's criteria.

> *Note: **Grade Beams** are underground beams connecting columns. They are used in challenging soils condition or in **Moment Frame** Design. Sometimes your structure may need to use **Moment Frame** for a storefront because there may not be enough horizontal length of **shear walls** for your building along the storefront direction to resist the lateral seismic force.*

6) Check and make sure the proper slab and sidewalk thickness and rebar size and spacing are specified per the soils report and the tenant's criteria in the details.

7) Have isolation joints between the sidewalk and masonry wall been shown?

ST2.0   Framing Details

Checklist:

1) Check and make sure the structural engineer uses <u>the proper, typical detail sheet</u>. I.e., if your building is metal stud construction, s/he should be using a metal stud construction detail sheet; if your building is wood stud construction, s/he should be using a wood stud construction detail sheet.

2) Check and make sure the <u>guardrail</u> on the retaining wall <u>matches architectural details</u>.

3) Check and make sure the proper <u>roof opening</u> details are included.

4) Check and make sure the proper <u>suspended **curtain wall details**</u> are included.

> *Note: At least two **curtain wall details** are needed in most cases: one for the suspended curtain wall <u>parallel</u> to the roof joists and the other for the suspended curtain wall <u>perpendicular</u> to the roof joists.*

5) Check and make sure the <u>metal stud wall height and gauge</u> **schedule** is included, if needed.

6) Check and make sure the parapet <u>brace detail</u> matches architectural details, and <u>proper blocking</u> is called out at the toe of the brace below the roof sheathing and between the roof joists.

7) For <u>full</u> height <u>metal</u> stud walls, s/he probably needs to use **slip track** at the top of the studs to accommodate the <u>expansion</u> of the studs.

8) Check and make sure curbs for rooftop HVAC units match architectural and mechanical details.

9) Check and make sure curbs for pilasters and canopy columns match architectural details. Are curbs designed as a separate pour from the columns and pilasters base?

ST3.0   Framing Details

See the checklist for Sheet ST2.0.

S1.0   Foundation Plans

Checklist:

1) Check and make sure <u>grid lines and dimensions</u> match the architectural floor plans.
2) Check and make sure the <u>footing schedule</u> and <u>slab schedule</u> match the soils report recommendation and the tenant's criteria.
3) Check and make sure the <u>graphics</u> of the foundation plan match the architectural floor plan.
4) Check and make sure ALL <u>retaining walls</u> for patios, landings, and so on, are shown and details are referenced.
5) Check and make sure ALL <u>deepened</u> footing and <u>retaining conditions</u> at the perimeter of the building are shown. Coordinate with the architectural floor plan and <u>civil grading plan</u> for <u>grades</u> adjacent to the building.

Note: You as an architect should send the <u>civil grading plan</u> to the structural engineer at the <u>beginning</u> of the project (or as soon as it is available) for his coordination.

6) Check footing, <u>grade beams</u>, etc., against the architectural floor plan and <u>plumbing</u> plan to make sure there are no <u>conflicts with floor drains, floor sinks, area drains</u>, etc.
7) Has your structural engineer shown and dimensioned exterior wall masonry expansion joints?
8) Use <u>"L"</u>-shaped footing along <u>adjacent</u> buildings or along property lines/parcel lines.
9) You may need to have deepened footing along adjacent buildings to make the <u>bottom of your footing align with</u> the bottom of adjacent buildings' footing to avoid discharge from the higher footing.
10) Can interior structural columns fit within the interior partition?

Note: This is very critical. For example, a 6" x 6" <u>steel</u> column can fit within a 2 x 6 <u>metal</u> stud wall, while a <u>6" x 6"</u> steel column may <u>NOT</u> fit within a 2 x 6 <u>wood</u> stud wall. Why? Because the actual dimension of the 2 x 6 wood stud is <u>1½" x 5½"</u>, and the 2 x 6 <u>wood</u> stud is just a <u>nominal</u> dimension. On the other hand, a 2" x 6" <u>metal</u> stud is the <u>actual</u> dimension.

This is <u>extremely critical</u> for bathrooms and hallways: If you design your hallway to have 5'-0" <u>clear</u> width, you need to <u>double check</u> to make sure you will actually get the 5'-0" clear width after you subtract all the structural elements and the gypsum board thickness, etc.

11) Have <u>control joints</u> (or <u>tooled joints</u>) and <u>construction joints</u> (or <u>expansion joints</u>) been shown at the correct spacing? Again, <u>expansion joints</u> shall be placed at 20'-0" O.C. max., while <u>tooled joints</u> shall be placed at 6'-0" O.C. max.

12) If a 6" concrete curb is used at the sill of exterior stud walls per architectural plans, then structural plans shall match this condition.

S2.0   Framing Plans

Checklist:

1) Have the roof hatch, HVAC, and other <u>roof openings</u> been shown to match the architectural plan and HVAC plan?
2) Do the <u>locations</u> and <u>weights</u> of HVAC units match the mechanical HVAC schedule and plan and the architectural roof plan?
3) Do the <u>locations</u> of braces match architectural roof plans? Make sure braces do not conflict with roof hatches or other elements.
4) Has structural support (blocking, etc.) been provided for mansard canopies and towers?
5) Are there any conflicts between structural members and roof drains as well as overflow drains?
6) Has the structural engineer added <u>blocking</u> (4 x 8 is typical) to support the roof drain and overflow drain pan?
7) Do NOT show T.O.S. or T.O.P. elevations on structural plans; add a note to refer to the architectural roof plan for this information instead. Normally, you <u>do NOT</u> want to <u>duplicate</u> the same information twice in a CD set. If you do, then you create a chance for conflicts when you update the plans later.
8) Coordinate structural members' depth with HVAC ducts' depth and electrical lights' thickness to make sure <u>each</u> room can achieve the intended <u>clear</u> ceiling heights.
9) Have glulam beams cambers been shown?
10) Provide dimensions (from grid lines) for glulam beams cantilever.

S3.0   **Sections**

Checklist:

1) Have the diagonal <u>braces</u> been placed <u>high enough</u> to clear the ceiling line and the track for the loading dock overhead doors if panelized doors are used?
2) Are the diagonal braces within the canopy attic <u>blocking the catwalk</u> access?
3) Have <u>blockings</u> been provided for the parapet braces?
4) Have <u>openings</u> been provided <u>for signage access</u> at the canopy <u>shear</u> wall and parapet?
5) Verify all <u>dimensions</u> and <u>section profiles</u> against the architectural sections.
6) Are roof sheathing heights shown correctly in <u>graphic</u> and match architectural sections and roof plan?
7) Do the radiuses, sizes, and shapes of column and pilaster concrete <u>bases</u> match architectural sections and details?

S3.1   **Sections**

See the checklist above.

b. Coordination of Electrical Drawings

E0.0   **Electrical Notes & Details**

Checklist:

1) Check <u>power service</u> (200 amp, 600 amp, or 800 amp; 120/208v, 277/480v, etc.) provided on a single-line diagram and notes to make sure it meets minimum power service required by the tenant's criteria.
2) <u>Mounting heights</u> for wall-mounted light fixtures match architectural elevations, and vice versa.

E0.1   **Electrical Notes & Details**

See the checklist above.

E0.2   **Electrical Title 24**

Checklist:

1) Make sure your electrical engineer <u>signs</u> the T-24 "<u>Certificate of Compliance</u>" in addition to stamping and signing all sheets for the submittal package.

E1.0   Power Plans & Panel Schedules

Checklist:

1) Check power service (200 amp, 600 amp, or <u>800 amp</u>; <u>120/208v, 277/480v</u>, etc.) provided on each panel schedule to make sure it meets <u>minimum</u> power service required by the tenant's criteria.
2) Coordinate with the mechanical plans for <u>numbers</u> and <u>locations</u> of HVAC units and provide <u>power</u> to them. Check power requirements of HVAC units (<u>120/208v</u> or <u>277/480v</u>) on mechanical schedules against electrical sheets to make sure they match.
3) Check the proper number of <u>outlets</u> provided at spacing per codes and tenant's criteria. 6'-0" or 10'-0" O.C. max. is typical.
4) Has <u>power</u> been provided for the fire sprinkler riser (<u>FSR</u>)?

E2.0   Lighting Plans

Checklist:

1) Check to make sure ALL light fixtures <u>inside</u> (2 x 4 lights, strip lights, track lights, down lights, etc.) and <u>outside</u> (canopy lights, soffit lights, wall-mounted lights, etc.) of the building <u>match the architectural</u> reflected ceiling plan in terms of numbers and locations.

   Note: This is very easy to do. You just need to use a <u>highlighter</u> to highlight each light fixture after you check it.

2) Check to make sure <u>NO</u> light fixture is in conflict with HVAC registers or ceiling access panels, etc.
3) <u>Self-powered exit signs</u> (often with two power sources) are shown at all legal exits and <u>match</u> architectural sheets.
4) Check to make sure <u>"J" boxes</u> are provided <u>for signs</u>.

c. Coordination of Mechanical Drawings

M0.0   Equipment Schedules, Notes, and Details

Checklist:

1) Correct <u>tonnage</u>, <u>brand</u> (Carrier, Lennox, etc.), and <u>type</u> of HVAC unit (all electric heat pumps or gas electrical) are provided per owner and the tenant's criteria.

M1.0   **Mechanical (or HVAC) Floor Plan and T-24 Energy Form**

Checklist:

1) HVAC ducts will <u>fit</u> in the attic space between the ceiling and roof framing members.
2) Check HVAC supply and return registers and exhaust fans and make sure they are <u>NOT in conflict with</u> electrical <u>light fixtures</u> and <u>match the architectural</u> ceiling plans.
3) <u>Undercut</u> the toilet room door <u>1"</u> and provide an exhaust fan OR provide both supply and return air registers.
4) <u>Flexible</u> ducts shall be <u>6'-0"</u> long max.
5) All ducts shall be <u>galvanized</u> and wrapped in <u>insulation</u>.

d. Coordination of Plumbing Drawings

P0.0   **Plumbing Schedules, Notes, Legend, and Details**

Checklist:

1) <u>Check the plumbing schedule against the plumbing plan</u>. Just read it carefully once and check it against the plumbing plan and you probably can find some conflicts, like the symbols or call-outs that do not match plan, etc.

P1.0   **Plumbing Floor Plans**

Checklist:

1) Coordinate plumbing line locations with architectural sheets. Try to <u>conceal plumbing lines</u> in stud walls whenever possible. You may need to go back and add <u>furring for CMU or tilt-up walls</u> on architectural sheets to <u>conceal</u> plumbing lines at areas visible to the public.
2) Coordinate <u>numbers and locations</u> of roof drains and overflow drains with architectural roof plans.
3) Coordinate <u>floor drains, floor sinks,</u> and <u>underground plumbing lines</u> with the structural foundation plan, and make sure there is no conflict; i.e., a floor sink is placed at a footing or grade beam location, etc.
4) Coordinate with mechanical plans for <u>numbers</u> and <u>locations</u> of HVAC units and provide <u>water and/or gas</u> to them.
5) Do the size of waterlines, water meters, sewer lines, gas lines, and gas meters meet the tenant's criteria?
6) Coordinate with the civil plans for <u>points of connection</u> (P.O.C.) for waterlines, sewer lines, etc.

7) Coordinate with the <u>gas company</u> and tenant for the <u>size and location</u> of gas meters. You probably need to forward them a copy of the plumbing plans.

8) <u>Connecting the roof drain (R.D.) to storm drains (SD) is a good design</u>, but you should confirm with the owner. Sometimes the owner simply wants to drain the roof drain under the sidewalk and though the <u>curb faces</u> to save money.

9) <u>Hose bibbs</u> are shown around the building (place them at <u>100' O.C.</u>, if possible). Use recessed wall hydrants at locations exposed to the public view, OR hide them on the back of the canopy columns.

e. Coordination of Architectural Sheets

This step can be done last. You can use the checklists for each architectural sheet mentioned earlier to do the checking.

C. Site Development Construction Drawings

A Site Development CD set may include architectural drawings, site electrical drawings, landscape drawings, and civil drawings (they can be under a separate contract). Sometimes utilities drawings from utilities firms are also included for reference.

1. Sheet Index for a Site Development CD set

The following is a sample Sheet Index for a **Site Development CD set**:

Table 5.6   **Sample Sheet Index for a Site Development CD Set**

Architectural

A0.0	Title Sheet
GN1.0	Accessibility Requirements
GN2.0	General Note
AS1.0	Architectural Site Plan
AS2.0	Site Details
AS3.0	Site Details

Electrical

E0.0	Electrical Notes & Details
E0.1	Electrical Notes & Details
E0.2	Site Electrical Title 24
E1.0	Power Plans & Panel Schedules
E2.0	Site Lighting Plan
E2.1	Site Photometric Plan

Landscape

L0.0	Landscape Notes & Details
LI.1	Landscape Irrigation Plan
LI.2	Landscape Irrigation Legend, Notes & Details
LP.1	Landscape Planting Plan
LP.2	Landscape Plant Legend, Notes & Details
LS.1	Landscape Specifications

Civil (it can be under separate contract)

C0.0	Civil Notes & Details
C0.1	A.D.A. Accessible Parking Data
C0.2	Boundary & Topographic Survey
C0.3	On-Site Demolition Plan
C1.0	Grading, Paving & Drainage Plan Notes & Details
C1.1	Grading & Drainage Plan Details
C1.2	Site Grading & Drainage Plan
C2.0	Horizontal Control Plan
C3.0	On-Site Storm Drain Plan
C4.0	Erosion Control/Stormwater Pollution Prevention Plan or SWPPP Plan
C5.0	Utility Plan Notes & Details
C5.1	On-Site Utility Plan

Let us discuss what information should go on each sheet:

2. Architectural <u>Sheet-by-Sheet</u> Checklist

Architectural

A0.0   Title Sheet

Checklist for a typical title sheet:

1) Your project name and address (street address, city, and state)
2) Contact information for your client and consultants and your firm
3) Sheet Index (see above)
4) <u>General Notes</u>

5) Vicinity map with north arrow pointing upward (you can get it from maps.yahoo.com or draw a simple line drawing with street names)
6) Legend: a few commonly used graphic symbols, such as keynote, revision delta, detail reference, etc.
7) Abbreviation: See detailed discussion in Chapter One. You just need to pick the terms related to Site Development.

GN1.0   Accessibility Requirements

See the checklist for Sheet GN1.0 in the building CD set.

GN2.0   General Note

See the checklist for Sheet GN2.0 in the building CD set.

AS1.0   Architectural Site Plan

Checklist:

1) Use **keynotes** instead of directly adding notes to the site plan. This way, the site plan will be much easier to read.
2) Handicap accessible path of travel from public sidewalks to the accessible entrances and emergency exits of your building. Add a note indicating the sidewalk slope shall be 5% or less, and cross slope for sidewalks shall be 2% or less.
3) Show handicap ramps and related railings and curb ramps, if needed.
4) Show zero curbs.
5) Building numbers and names but NO square footages; use dashed lines to show the shape of proposed buildings.
6) Use redwood headers to enclose future building pads.
7) Property lines
8) Setback line and easements
9) Parcel lines
10) Parking stalls and numbers of stalls
11) Trash enclosures and trash compactors
12) Show central mail delivery and mailbox locations: specify manufacturer, model, and locations.
13) Show bicycle racks and trash receptacles: specify manufacturer, model, and locations.
14) Pylon and monument signs. Clearly define what portion of the sign is done by the sign contractor and what portion is done by the site contractor. The site contractor will normally provide electrical hookups for all signs.

15) Pole-mounted handicap entrances and stop signs are typically done by the site contractor.

16) Loading docks: excavation of the loading dock shall be part of the site contract.

17) Fire truck access paths and major dimensions per fire department. 25' wide minimum fire truck lane is common. Check with your fire department.

18) Streets, street names, and turning radius

19) Traffic guide signals painted on AC paving and/or curbs: stop signs, directional arrows, dashed traffic lines, and "NO PARKING—FIRE LANE" letters, red curbs, etc. Verify locations, letter sizes, and lengths with the fire department.

20) It is common to paint most of the items on the site with two coats of highway paint, and the most common colors are white (for bollards, parking stall stripings (NOT strippings), traffic guide signals, stop signs, directional arrows, dashed traffic lines, curbs, etc.), yellow (for bollards, parking stall stripings, traffic guide signals, stop signs, directional arrows, dashed traffic lines, curbs, etc.), blue (for handicap parking stalls and signs), and red (for red curbs, bollards, etc.). You need to verify the colors with the city and the fire department.

21) Parking stall stripings and dashed traffic lines typically use two coats of 4" wide highway paint.

22) Sidewalks, stoops, and stairs

23) Light poles, bases, transformers, and related concrete pads. You can wblock them from your electrical engineer's plans when they are available.

24) Note pylon and monument signs and building signs are shown for reference only, and they are under a separate permit and approval.

25) North arrow and scale (1" = 100'-0" is common)

26) Dimensions to locate all buildings and site features to the property lines

27) Site detail references

28) Major **site technical data**: see Sample on Sheet AS1.0 in the building CD set.

29) Coordinate with landscape plans: Hardscape features, trees and other landscape features. You can wblock them from your landscape architect's plans when they are available. Check the form, habit, height, and density of your trees and make sure they will NOT block the signage of your buildings. Landscape islands at parking areas shall be 4'-0" wide minimum and 5'-0" wide preferred. Some cities require them to be 5'-0" wide minimum. Call the cities to confirm.

30) Coordinate with civil plans: boundary & topographic survey plans for property lines and easement, horizontal control plans for dimensions, grading plans for grades and handicap (accessible) path of travel, drainage plans for storm drains and catch basin locations and points of connections (P.O.C.) and concrete swales, curbs, and gutters, and utility plans for P.O.C.s for utilities (gas, water, fire sprinkler

31) lines, sewer lines, etc.).Provide utility markers at all utility line stub-up locations.

32) Coordinate with site electrical plans: site lighting plans for locations and number of <u>lights</u>, and power plans for <u>transformer</u> and <u>switchgear</u> locations and <u>size</u> and power connections to <u>monument signs</u>.

33) Use dashed lines to show building canopy columns and overhang lines.

34) Use dashed lines to show <u>NIC</u> and <u>off-site</u> items and proposed <u>future</u> items.

35) Use keynotes to indicate that the contractor should provide rough grading and compaction for the entire proposed <u>building area</u> and <u>10'-0"</u> beyond (including the canopy) per soils report's recommendation.

36) Coordinate the buildings' outlines, entrances and exits, and scope of work with the building CD set.

AS2.0   Site Details

Checklist:

1) Show details for <u>expansion joints</u> (or construction joints) and <u>tooled joints</u> (or <u>control joints</u>), wheel stops (if any), light pole bases, bollards, handicap signs, redwood headers, utility markers, curb ramps, ramps, handrails and guardrails, parking stalls (check with the city to find out if <u>single striping or double striping</u> is required), and trash enclosures, etc.

2) Contact the city for standard details. Many <u>cities</u> have <u>standard details</u> or at least diagrams for the above-mentioned items.

3) Concrete curb/swale details shall be shown by the civil plans.

4) Coordinate details with the <u>tenant's criteria</u>: colors for parking stall stripings, reinforcement and thickness for sidewalks, size and shape for curbs and swales, etc.

5) Have your <u>structural engineer review</u> and mark up the <u>rebars</u> for the trash enclosure walls and foundation and retaining walls.

AS3.0   Site Details

See the checklist for Sheet AS2.0.

3. Electrical <u>Sheet-by-Sheet</u> Checklist

E0.0   Electrical Notes & Details

Checklist:

1) Check the <u>power service</u> (200 amp, 600 amp, or 800 amp; 120/208v, 277/480v, etc.) provided on <u>single-line diagrams</u> for each building on the site and <u>notes</u> to make sure it meets the minimum power service required by various tenants' criteria.

E0.1   Electrical Notes & Details

See the checklist above.

E0.2   Site Electrical Title 24

Checklist:

1) Make sure your electrical engineer <u>signs</u> the T-24 "<u>Certificate of Compliance</u>" in addition to stamping and signing all sheets for the submittal package.

E1.0   Power Plans & Panel Schedules

Checklist:

1) Check the power service (200 amp, 600 amp, or <u>800 amp</u>; <u>120/208v</u>, <u>277/480v</u>, etc.) provided on each panel schedule to make sure it meets the <u>minimum</u> power service required by various tenants' criteria.
2) Has <u>power</u> been provided for the pylon sign and monument sign?
3) Coordinate and make sure site power plans match the <u>latest</u> architectural site plan.
4) Coordinate with the architect regarding the locations of <u>transformers and switchgears</u>.
5) Provide <u>secondary power lines</u> from the transformer to within <u>5'-0"</u> of the buildings. Coordinate with the developer, tenant, and the architect regarding the locations.
6) Provide telephone <u>lines</u> and cable TV <u>lines</u> (if required by the developer or the tenant) to within <u>5'-0"</u> of the buildings. Coordinate with the developer, tenant, and the architect regarding the locations.
7) Provide power, cable TV, and telephone <u>conduits</u> and <u>stub and cap</u> them at <u>2'-0"</u> into the <u>future</u> building pads. Coordinate with the developer, tenant, and the architect regarding the locations.
8) Provide a waterproof "J" box at the <u>post indicator vale</u> locations and ¾" <u>conduits</u> from the "J" box to the building's fire sprinkler riser (FSR) locations.
9) Place <u>pull boxes</u> at the proper locations to avoid conflicts with the planter, signs, etc.
10) Provide <u>heavy-duty cover for pull boxes</u> at heavy traffic areas.
11) <u>Conduit runs</u> shall avoid future building locations.
12) Coordinate with the electrical engineer to get the <u>engineered underground distribution plan</u> from the power company and include it in the bid package.

E2.0   Site Lighting Plans

Checklist:

1) Has lighting met the minimum and maximum <u>foot-candle requirements</u> of the tenants and the city?
2) Light poles shall not be in conflict with storm drains, <u>underground</u> utilities lines, and planters.
3) Lights in <u>future</u> building pad areas shall be connected to future buildings.
4) Provide power and waterproof "J" box for landscape <u>irrigation controller</u> and <u>pylon signs</u>.
5) Use a <u>shield</u> for light fixtures near the property line to deflect light to adjacent properties and the sky to reduce **light pollution**.
6) Coordinate with the city, developer, various tenants, architect, and structural engineer regarding the <u>light pole heights</u>.
7) Add a note to "Refer to <u>architectural and structural</u> drawings for more information for light pole base."
8) Verify with the city, developer, various tenants, and architect regarding the light fixture selection.
9) Verify with the owner and stub site lighting conduits into future building pads for future lights.

E2.1   Site Photometric Plan

Checklist:

1) Check to make sure the minimum and maximum lighting level or foot-candles shown on the site photometric plan meet the tenant's criteria.
2) Coordinate with your electrical engineer to pick the right site lighting fixtures and make sure they meet the criteria of the city, tenant, and owner.
3) This sheet can often be generated by the lighting manufacturer's representative for "free." You just need to coordinate with your electrical engineer and have him contact the manufacturer's representative of the site light fixture that he specified. The manufacturer's representative can often do this very quickly for free if you specify their products.

4. Landscape <u>Sheet-by-Sheet</u> Checklist

L0.0   Landscape Notes & Details

Checklist:

1) Read the entire sheet <u>at least once</u>, word-for-word and line-by-line.
2) Check the landscape sheet index against actual sheets.

LI.1   Landscape Irrigation Plan

Checklist:

1) Check to make sure ALL planting areas (PA), including <u>planters within sidewalks,</u> are provided with **head-to-head** irrigation.
2) Coordinate with the <u>civil</u> engineer and have him provide properly sized <u>landscape meters.</u>
3) Avoid placing planters right next to the building: provide at least a <u>1-foot-wide concrete mowing strip</u> next to the building, if possible.
4) Show irrigation <u>controller</u> and coordinate with the architect for the <u>location</u> and with electrical engineer for <u>power requirements.</u>
5) Provide a **backflow prevention device** when required by the city or codes.
6) Check to make sure the landscape irrigation plan has been <u>updated</u> per the <u>latest</u> architectural site plan.

LI.2   Landscape Irrigation Legend, Notes & Details

Checklist:
1) Read the entire sheet <u>at least once,</u> word-for-word and line-by-line.
2) Check to make sure every detail has been referenced.

LP.1   Landscape Planting Plan

Checklist:

1) Check to make sure ALL planting areas (PA), including <u>planters within sidewalks,</u> are covered with <u>plants.</u>
2) Check the form, habit, mature height, spread, and density of trees to make sure they will <u>NOT block</u> the building or pylon or monument <u>signs.</u>
3) Landscape <u>setback</u> areas at property lines.
4) Provide proper landscape screening for electrical transformers, trash enclosures, loading docks, and other unsightly elements.
5) Show landscape redwood headers at the perimeter of future building pads and street landscape setback areas.
6) Coordinate tree locations with light poles, signs, etc., to make sure there is no conflict.
7) Coordinate with civil to show contour for new landscape mounding areas.

LP.2   Landscape Plant Legend, Notes & Details

Checklist:

1) Read the entire sheet at least once, word-for-word and line-by-line.
2) Check to make sure every detail has been referenced.

LS.1   Landscape Specifications

Checklist:

1) Read the entire sheet at least once, word-for-word and line-by-line.
2) Check the separate specifications book to coordinate the landscape specifications portion. It may be a good idea to put all the landscape specifications at one location, either in the specifications book or on the landscape specifications sheet, NOT at both places. You can add notes in the separate specifications book to "Refer to landscape specifications sheet for landscape specifications" if you are placing ALL the information on the sheet, and vice versa.

5. Civil Sheet-by-Sheet Checklist
(Civil engineering can be under a separate contract.)

C0.0   Civil Notes & Details

Checklist:

1) Read the entire sheet at least once, word-for-word and line-by-line.
2) Check to make sure every detail has been referenced.

C0.1   A.D.A. Accessible Parking Data

Checklist:

1) Read the entire sheet at least once, word-for-word and line-by-line.
2) Coordinate with architectural handicap notes and details.
3) Coordinate with the tenant's criteria.

C0.2   Boundary & Topographic Survey

Checklist:

1) Read the entire sheet at least once, word-for-word and line-by-line.

2) Coordinate with the architectural site plan and landscape site plan and find out if any of the <u>existing trees and existing site features</u> can be saved.

C0.3   On-Site Demolition Plan

Checklist:

1) Read the entire sheet <u>at least once</u>, word-for-word and line-by-line.
2) Use keynotes instead of adding notes directly to the plan.

C1.0   Grading, Paving & Drainage Plan Notes & Details

Checklist:

1) Read the entire sheet <u>at least once</u>, word-for-word and line-by-line.
2) Coordinate with the tenant's criteria.

C1.1   Grading & Drainage Plan Details

Checklist:

1) <u>8%</u> maximum slope for the entry driveway from the street, if possible.
2) Sidewalks and hardscape shall slope at <u>1% to 2%</u> away from the building; <u>1.5%</u> is preferred.
3) <u>2 %</u> maximum <u>cross</u> slope for the sidewalk.
4) Design the sidewalk slope at less than 5% to avoid ramps, if possible.
5) Design all ramps to slope <u>between 6.67% and 8.33%</u> whenever possible to <u>avoid</u> the use of <u>truncated domes</u>. Verify with your city. Some cities will require truncated domes for <u>ALL</u> ramps, regardless of the slope.
6) Try to use a <u>3%</u> maximum <u>cross</u> slope for AC paving at the truck service drive.
7) Use a <u>1% to 3%</u> slope for AC paving at <u>typical</u> parking areas, if possible.
8) Use a <u>2%</u> maximum slope in any direction at the <u>handicap</u> parking stall and adjacent aisles, if possible.
9) Show all building <u>finish elevations</u>, pad elevations, and <u>future</u> building <u>finish elevations</u> and <u>pad elevations</u>; verify the pad elevations against <u>the slab and base thickness</u> suggested by the soils report.

   Note: This is important. For example, the soils report may suggest 5" concrete slab over 15 mil moisture barrier over 6" crushed rocks. So, the total <u>slab and base thickness is 5" + 6" =11"</u>, then if your building finish elevation is <u>21'-0"</u>, the pad elevation will be (21'-0") – 11" = 20'-1" or <u>20.08'</u>.

Therefore, if your civil engineer shows a 20.50' pad elevation on the grading plan, then you KNOW it is wrong, and you should have him correct it per the soils report.

10) 0.05% minimum slope for the concrete swale or gutter
11) If you are using thresholds, then spot elevations for ALL entrances and exits shall match the building finish floor elevation. Slope the finished surface away from buildings at 1.5%.
12) If you are NOT using thresholds, then spot elevations for entrances and exits WITHOUT thresholds shall be ½", or 0.04' below building finish floor elevation.
13) Exterior spot elevations are shown at every corner of the buildings.
14) Show existing contours as dashed lines, and new contours as solid lines.

Note: The intervals of the contour shall be 1'-0", and use darker lines at 5'-0" intervals. This is a standard practice in civil engineering.

15) Check AC paving sections against the soils report recommendation.
16) Coordinate with the building CD set regarding the scope of the work for site and for building contracts.
17) Excavation of the loading dock truck well and ramp shall be part of the site work.
18) Coordinate with the architect regarding retaining wall locations and provide proper details.
19) Show invert and top of grate elevations at storm drain catch basins.

C1.2   Site Grading & Drainage Plan

See the checklist for Sheet C1.1

C2.0   Horizontal Control Plan

Checklist:

1) Use bearings and distances (**"mete and bounds"**) to show property lines. If you are drawing the property line in CAD and you draw everything correctly per the bearings and distances, the property line should close at the end. If it does not close, you probably made a mistake.
2) Coordinate with the architectural site plan regarding ALL dimensions.
3) Tie dimensions to property lines.
4) Coordinate with the structural engineer and architect and show properly sized seismic gaps between the buildings. 6" or 8" or 12" gaps are typical, depending on the height of adjacent buildings.
5) Show radiuses for ALL curbs and concrete planters.
6) Use dashed lines to show future buildings and parking stalls.
7) Use redwood headers to enclose future building pads.

8) <u>Coordinate</u> ALL items against the architectural site plans, i.e., decorative pavement, building shapes and sizes, planters, sidewalks, etc. Use a highlighter and highlight each item as you check the plan.

C3.0   On-Site Storm Drain Plan

Checklist:

1) Check <u>P.O.C.</u> for ALL storm drain (SD) lines against the architectural site plan and building floor plan and roof plan.
2) Make sure SD lines do not conflict with light poles, transformers, planters, trash enclosures, etc.
3) Stub storm drain lines to <u>within 5'-0"</u> of the building.
4) Coordinate with the <u>tenant's criteria</u> and building CD architectural and <u>plumbing</u> plans for all roof drain lines and overflow drain lines' <u>locations and sizes</u>. This is an important coordination item at the <u>beginning</u> of the project.

C4.0   Erosion Control/Stormwater Pollution Prevention Plan or SWPPP

Checklist:

1) Read the entire sheet <u>at least once</u>, word-for-word and line-by-line.
2) Incorporate LEED criteria, if possible, even when your building may not be seeking LEED certification.

C5.0   Utility Plan Notes & Details

Checklist:

1) Read the entire sheet <u>at least once</u>, word-for-word and line-by-line.

C5.1   On-Site Utility Plan

Checklist:

1) Sometimes the utility plans are divided into <u>dry</u> utility plans (gas, electricity, etc.) and <u>wet</u> utility plans (water, fire service lines, etc.).
2) <u>Dimension</u> and locate P.O.C. for utilities lines.
3) Stub waterlines and all other utility lines (fire sprinkler lines, sewer lines, etc.) to <u>within 5'-0"</u> of the building and <u>2'-0" into</u> future building pads.

4) Verify with the developer and tenant and find out if one water meter is adequate for each building OR if each tenant will need a separate water meter.

5) Coordinate with the landscape irrigation plans for water meter size and location.

6) Try to use 1½" water meters for 2" waterlines, if possible, because 2" or bigger water meters will probably cost a lot more in fees when you apply for a permit in the city and get connection at a utility company.

7) Water meters are part of the civil scope of work. Plumbing plans and landscape irrigation plans may show them for reference only.

8) Civil plans shall show the fire sprinkler system to within 5'-0" of buildings, including required valves like P.I.V.'s, detector check valves, etc.

9) Coordinate with the tenant's criteria and building CD architectural and plumbing plans for all utility line locations and sizes. This is an important coordination item at the beginning of the project.

10) Show fire hydrants (F.H.) per fire department requirements.

11) Use a sump pump or gravity drain (connecting to storm drain) for the trench drain or catch basin at loading dock truck wells. The sump pump shall be part of the building contract, and the building electrical engineer will need to provide power for it.

12) If a building has a food service (restaurants, etc.), grease interceptors shall be provided as part of the building contract. Show them as dashed lines on civil plans for reference only.

D. Specifications: What to Do and What to Look for When Reviewing and Editing a Typical Set of Specifications?

Specifications show quality, standards, and workmanship of project elements, including materials, equipment, systems, etc.

See the discussion on MasterFormat in Chapter One for more information.

Once you set up a typical set of specifications for your office, you can save as and reuse them for future projects.

When you start to write a set of specifications for a project, the following are some basic steps:

First, you need to review your typical specifications and cross out the sections that are NOT used.

Second, you need to send some specifications sections to the owner and consultants for review. Below are some abbreviations and information about which specifications sections need to go to whom for review:

O – Owner
C – Civil Engineer
L – Landscape Architect
S – Structural Engineer
E – Electrical Engineer
M – Mechanical Engineer
P – Plumbing Engineer

Third, you need to review ALL the specifications sections that you are actually using and tailor them to your project, and you also need to review the owner's and your consultants' markup for their specifications sections. As an architect, you need to review ALL specifications sections and coordinate them. You are the one looking at the overall picture.

There are only a few specifications sections that will require revisions in most cases, but make sure you read the specifications at least once, word-for-word and line-by-line, and modify each section if needed per your specific project requirements.

If the tenant wants you to use their prototype specifications, just use their prototype specifications and supplement them with your own master specifications for the missing sections ONLY.

Do NOT use both the tenant's prototype specifications and entire set of your master specifications because you do NOT want to have duplicated specifications sections and the related confusion.

The following are some tips on reviewing and modifying some specification sections:

Table 5.7   Tips on Reviewing and Modifying Some Specification Sections

Division 1		General Requirements (New Version Division Number: 01 00 00)
	01100	Summary
	01200	Price and Payment Procedures
	01300	Administrative Requirements
	01400	Quality Requirements
	01500	Temporary Facilities and Controls
	01600	Product Requirements
	01700	Execution Requirements
	01800	Facility Operation
	01900	Facility Decommissioning

Note:
Make sure you send all specification sections under Division 1 to the owner for his review.

Facility Construction Subgroup:

Division 2   Site Construction **(New Version: Division 02 00 00 Existing Condition)**

02050   Basic Site Materials and Methods (for C review)

02100   Site Remediation (for C review)

02200   Site Preparation (for C review)

02300   Earthwork (for C review)

02400   Tunneling, Boring, and Jacking

02450   Foundation and Load-Bearing Elements (for S review)

02500   Utility Services (for C/E/P review)

02600   Drainage and Containment (for C review)

02700   Bases, Ballasts, Pavements, and Appurtenances (for C review)

02800   Site Improvements and Amenities (for C review)

02900   Planting (for L review)

02950   Site Restoration and Rehabilitation (for C review)

Division 3   Concrete **(New Version Division Number: 03 00 00)**

03050   Basic Concrete Materials and Methods

*Note: For **S** review, pay attention to concrete flatness. For example, most retail buildings can have **concrete flatness** of ¼" per 10'-0", but some major tenants do require concrete flatness of ⅛" per 10'-0".*

03100   Concrete Forms and Accessories (for S review)

03200   Concrete Reinforcement (for S review)

03300   Cast-In-Place Concrete (for S review)

03400   Precast Concrete (for S review)

03500   Cementitious Decks and Underlayment (for S review)

03600   Grouts (for S review)

03700   Mass Concrete (for S review)

03900   Concrete Restoration and Cleaning (for S review)

Division 4   Masonry **(New Version Division Number: 04 00 00)**

04050   Basic Masonry Materials and Methods (for S review)

04200   Masonry Units (for S review)

04400   Stone (for S review)

04500   Refractories

04600   Corrosion-Resistant Masonry (for S review)

04700   Simulated Masonry (for S review)

04800   Masonry Assemblies (for S review)

04900   Masonry Restoration and Cleaning

Division 5   Metals **(New Version Division Number: 05 00 00)**

05050   Basic Metal Materials and Methods (for S review)

05100   Structural Metal Framing (for S review)

05200   Metal Joists (for S review)

05300   Metal Deck (for S review)

05400   Cold-Formed Metal Framing (for S review)

05500   Metal Fabrications (for S review)

05600   Hydraulic Fabrications (for S review)

05700   Ornamental Metal

05800   Expansion Control

05900   Metal Restoration and Cleaning

Division 6   Wood and Plastics **(New Version: Division 06 00 00 Wood, Plastics and Composites)**

06050   Basic Wood and Plastic Materials and Methods (for S review)

06100   Rough Carpentry (for S review)

06200   Finish Carpentry

06400   Architectural Woodwork

06500   Structural Plastics (for S review)

06600   Plastic Fabrications (for S review)

06900   Wood and Plastic Restoration and Cleaning

Division 7   Thermal and Moisture Protection **(New Version Division Number: 07 00 00)**

07050   Basic Thermal and Moisture Protection Materials and Methods

07100   Damproofing and Waterproofing

07200   Thermal Protection

07300   Shingles, Roof Tiles, and Roof Coverings

07400   Roofing and Siding Panels

07500   Membrane Roofing

07600   Flashing and Sheet Metal

07700   Roof Specialties and Accessories

07800   Fire and Smoke Protection

07900   Joint Sealers

Division 8   Doors and Windows **(New Version: Division 08 00 00 Openings)**

08050   Basic Door and Window Materials and Methods

08100   Metal Doors and Frames

08200   Wood and Plastic Doors

08300   Specialty Doors

08400   Entrances and Storefronts

*Note: Coordinate with the tenant's criteria and drawings, double check if ¼" glazing or 1" insulated glazing is being used. Check related entrances and storefronts and select the CORRECT model for the kind of the glazing that you are using. For example, **Kawneer** Trifab 400 is for ¼" glazing, while Trifab 451 is for 1" insulated glazing.*

08500   Windows

08600   Skylights

08700   Hardware

Note: Coordinate with the tenant's criteria and drawings regarding the manufacturer and model of the hardware being used.

08800   Glazing

08900   Glazed Curtain Wall

Division 9   Finishes **(New Version Division Number: 09 00 00)**

09050   Basic Finish Materials and Methods

09100   Metal Support Assemblies

09200   Plaster and Gypsum Board

09300   Tile

09400   Terrazzo

09500   Ceilings

Note: Coordinate with the tenant's criteria and drawings regarding the manufacturer and model.

09600   Flooring

09700   Wall Finishes

09800   Acoustical Treatment

09900   Paints and Coatings

Division 10   Specialties **(New Version Division Number: 10 00 00)**

10100   Visual Display Boards

10150   Compartments and Cubicles

10200   Louvers and Vents

10240   Grilles and Screens

10250   Service Walls

10260   Wall and Corner Guards

10270   Access Flooring

10290   Pest Control

10300   Fireplaces and Stoves

10340   Manufactured Exterior Specialties

10350   Flagpoles

10400   Identification Devices

10450   Pedestrian Control Devices

10500   Lockers

10520   Fire Protection Specialties

10530   Protective Covers

10550   Postal Specialties

10600   Partitions

10670   Storage Shelving

10700   Exterior Protection

	10750	Telephone Specialties
	10800	Toilet, Bath, and Laundry Specialties
	10880	Scales
	10900	Wardrobe and Closet Specialties

Division 11		**Equipment (New Version Division Number: 11 00 00)**
	11010	Maintenance Equipment
	11020	Security and Vault Equipment
	11030	Teller and Service Equipment (for E review)
	11040	Ecclesiastical Equipment
	11050	Library
	11060	Theater and Stage Equipment
	11070	Instrumental Equipment
	11080	Registration Equipment
	11090	Checkroom Equipment
	11100	Mercantile Equipment
	11110	Commercial Laundry and Dry Cleaning Equipment
	11120	Vending Equipment (for E review)
	11130	Audio-Visual Equipment (for E review)
	11140	Vehicle Service Equipment (for E review)
	11150	Parking Control Equipment (for E review)
	11160	Loading Dock Equipment (for E review)
	11170	Solid Waste Handling Equipment (for E review)
	11190	Detention Equipment
	11200	Water Supply and Treatment Equipment (for P review)
	11280	Hydraulic Gates and Valves (for P review)
	11300	Fluid Waste Treatment and Disposal Equipment (for E review)
	11400	Food Service Equipment (for E review)
	11450	Residential Equipment
	11460	Unit Kitchens (for E/M/P review)
	11470	Darkroom Equipment (for E review)
	11480	Athletic, Recreational, and Therapeutic Equipment (for E review)
	11500	Industrial and Process Equipment (for E review)
	11600	Laboratory Equipment (for E review)
	11650	Planetarium Equipment (for E review)
	11660	Observatory Equipment (for E review)
	11680	Office Equipment (for E review)
	11700	Medical Equipment (for E review)
	11780	Mortuary Equipment (for E review)
	11850	Navigation Equipment (for E review)
	11870	Agricultural Equipment
	11900	Exhibit Equipment

Division 12   Furnishings **(New Version Division Number: 12 00 00)**

12050	Fabrics
12100	Art
12300	Manufactured Casework
12400	Furnishings and Accessories
12500	Furniture
12600	Multiple Seating
12700	Systems Furniture
12800	Interior Plants and Planters (for L review)
12900	Furnishings Restoration and Repair

Division 13   Special Construction **(New Version Division Number: 13 00 00)**

13010	Air-Supported Structures (for S review)
13020	Building Modules (for S review)
13030	Special Purpose Rooms
13080	Sound, Vibration, and Seismic Control (for S review)
13090	Radiation Protection (for E/M review)
13100	Lightning Protection (for E review)
13110	Cathodic Protection
13120	Pre-Engineered Structures (for S review)
13150	Swimming Pools (for S/P/E review)
13160	Aquariums (for S/P review)
13165	Aquatic Park Facilities (for S/P review)
13170	Tubs and Pools (for S/P review)
13175	Ice Rinks (for E review)
13185	Kennels and Animal Shelters
13190	Site-Constructed Incinerators (for E review)
13200	Storage Tanks
13220	Filter Underdrains and Media (for P review)
13230	Digester Covers and Appurtenances
13240	Oxygenation Systems (for E review)
13260	Sludge Conditioning Systems (for E review)
13280	Hazardous Material Remediation
13400	Measurement and Control Instrumentation
13500	Recording Instrumentation (for E review)
13550	Transportation Control Instrumentation (for E/C review)
13600	Solar and Wind Energy Equipment (for E/M review)
13700	Security Access and Surveillance (for E review)
13800	Building Automation and Control (for E/M review)
13850	Detection and Alarm (for E review)
13900	Fire Suppression (for P review)

Division 14   Conveying Systems **(New Version: Division 14 00 00 Conveying Equipment)**

14100	Dumbwaiters
14200	Elevators (for S review)
14300	Escalators and Moving Walks (for S review)
14400	Lifts (for S review)
14500	Material Handling
14600	Hoists and Cables
14700	Turntables
14800	Scaffolding
14900	Transportation

Division 15
(For **M** review)   Mechanical **(In the New Version: Division 15 is changed to "Reserved for Future Expansion" and mechanical is spread as parts of Divisions 21 00 00, 22 00 00, 23 00 00, etc., of the New Version.)**

15050	Basic Mechanical Materials and Methods
15100	Building Service Piping
15200	Process Piping
15300	Fire Protection Piping
15400	Plumbing Fixtures and Equipment
15500	Heat-Generation Equipment
15600	Refrigeration Equipment
15700	Heating, Ventilating, and Air Conditioning Equipment
15800	Air Distribution
15900	HVAC Instrumentation and Controls
15950	Testing, Adjusting, and Balancing

Division 16
(For **E** review)   Electrical **(In New Version: Division 16 is changed to "Reserved for Future Expansion," and Electrical is spread as parts of Divisions 26 00 00, 27 00 00, and 28 00 00, etc., of the new version)**

16050	Basic Electrical Materials and Methods
16100	Wiring Methods
16200	Electrical Power
16300	Transmission and Distribution
16400	Low-Voltage Distribution
16500	Lighting
16700	Communications
16800	Sound and Video

New Version of MasterFormat also includes the following new divisions:

Division 17 00 00	**Reserved for Future Expansion**
Division 18 00 00	**Reserved for Future Expansion**

Facility Services Subgroup:

Division 20 00 00	**Reserved for Future Expansion**
Division 21 00 00	**Fire Suppression** (for P review)
Division 22 00 00	**Plumbing** (for P review)
Division 23 00 00	**Heating, Ventilation, and Air Conditioning** (for M review)
Division 24 00 00	**Reserved for Future Expansion**
Division 25 00 00	**Integrated Automation** (for E/M review)
Division 26 00 00	**Electrical** (for E review)
Division 27 00 00	**Communications** (for E review)
Division 28 00 00	**Electronic Safety and Security** (for E review)
Division 29 00 00	**Reserved for Future Expansion**

Site and Infrastructure Subgroup:

Division 30 00 00	**Reserved for Future Expansion**
Division 31 00 00	**Earthwork** (for C review)
Division 32 00 00	**Exterior Improvements**
Division 33 00 00	**Utilities** (for C/E/P review)
Division 34 00 00	**Transportation** (for C review)
Division 35 00 00	**Waterway and Marine** (for C review)
Division 36 00 00	**Reserved for Future Expansion**
Division 37 00 00	**Reserved for Future Expansion**
Division 38 00 00	**Reserved for Future Expansion**
Division 39 00 00	**Reserved for Future Expansion**

Process Equipment Subgroup:

Division 40 00 00	**Process Integration**
Division 41 00 00	**Material Processing and Handling Equipment** (for E review)
Division 42 00 00	**Process Heating, Cooling, and Drying Equipment** (for M review)
Division 43 00 00	**Process Gas and Liquid Handling, Purification and Storage Equipment** (for P review)

Division 44 00 00	**Pollution Control Equipment** (for E review)
Division 45 00 00	**Industry-Specific Manufacturing Equipment** (for E review)
Division 46 00 00	**Reserved for Future Expansion**
Division 47 00 00	**Reserved for Future Expansion**
Division 48 00 00	**Electrical Power Generation** (for E review)
Division 49 00 00	**Reserved for Future Expansion**

E. Plan Check Corrections, Site, and Building Permit: What to Do when Dealing with Plan Check Corrections? Permit Expiration Date and Pulling Permit.

Most projects will experience one or two plan check corrections before the permit is ready.

When you receive plan check corrections, **first of all**, you need to send out the plan check correction list and related plan check markup related to <u>consultants</u> so that the <u>consultants</u> can start to pick up the plan check items right away; **second**, you can pick up the <u>architectural portion</u> of the plan check corrections.

The turnaround time for updating CD sets per plan check corrections should be about 1 or 2 weeks unless the corrections are very extensive.

For most cities, once your site or building is permitted, <u>the construction needs to start within 1 year of the permit approval</u>. If you need more time after 1 year, you can probably pay a fee and ask for a <u>6-month or 1-year extension</u> of the permit, depending on the specific city's requirements.

Your client, you, and your team have put in a tremendous amount of time and effort to get the permit ready. Do NOT let the permit expire.

The permit is normally <u>pulled by the general contractor</u>, and the fees for pulling the permit are typically <u>paid by the developer or tenant</u> if the tenant, like some supermarkets, is building his own building, depending on how the construction contract is written.

Chapter Six

Bidding & Negotiation

A. Competitive Bid and Negotiated Bid

There are two basic forms of bid: Competitive Bid and Negotiated Bid.

In a **Competitive Bid**, several contractors are invited to bid on a project, OR bids can be opened to all contractors. The owner will then select one of the qualified bids. The advantage of competitive bids is that the initial price will probably be lower than negotiated bid because each bidder is under pressure to submit the lowest bid to get the project.

In a **Negotiated Bid**, the owner will select a qualified contractor with the help of an architect, and then negotiate with the contractor on the final contract price. The advantage of negotiated bids is that the owner can get the contractor involved from the very beginning of the project, even before the drawings and specifications are started. The contractor can give valuable input on the selection of the building system and the related costs, construction methods, etc. The owner will probably see fewer change orders because the contractor knows the project very well, and he is under less pressure to submit a very low bid to begin with.

Note: Owner does NOT have to select the lowest bid. It is typical for the owner to include in the invitation to bid documents that the owner has the right to select ANY bid, and the right to reject ANY and ALL bids.

This is because sometimes the lowest bid may NOT be the most qualified bid, and the project can be delayed or cancelled, so the owner needs to have a legal way to get out of signing ANY contract if the project is cancelled OR the owner decides not to build the project after reviewing the bids.

B. Public Bid Opening and Private Bid Opening

At a **Public Bid Opening**, each bid is read out aloud to all participating contractors, so everyone knows what the other contractors' bid is. At a **Private Bid Opening**, the owner will review the bids himself or with the architect, and then determine which contractor to use.

C. Various Bid Documents and Forms

1. Invitation to Bid

Invitation to Bid is a letter to invite contractors to bid on the project. If you are inviting five contractors to bid on a project, you should NOT write five different letters and address each letter to each contractor. You should write <u>ONE letter, address it to ALL five contractors</u>, and list ALL five contractors on the List of Distribution on the letter. You want to make sure <u>each bidder gets exactly the same information</u>.

Invitation to Bid should include the project name, location, project number, the due time and date and place of the bid, instructions to bidders on the cost of additional sets of plans and specifications, Plan Room contact information (if any Plan Room is used), and any other information or instructions they should be aware of. It should also describe whether the bid will be a public or a private opening. It should be dated like a normal letter, and you need to cc the owner and tenant.

*Note: A **Plan Room** is a room where ALL the subcontractors can go and review the plans and specifications. For example, **Builders Exchange** (www.gsbe.net) and **F. W. Dodger** (www.fwdodge.com) are two common Plan Rooms. A Plan Room may even put the bid documents online for bidders and subcontractors to review.*

2. Bid Proposal

Bid Proposal is a standard form prepared by the architect and filled out by all bidders. The following is a sample Bid Proposal Form:

Table 6.1   Sample Bid Proposal Form

Bid Proposal for Major Building A for American Retail, Inc.
Located at City of Anywhere, CA, USA

A+A Job #: 09388   **Date: 9/8/09**

Bid Proposal

Note: Each bidder shall fill out the Bid Proposal Form completely. Incomplete Bid Proposals may be disqualified.

Bidder:_____

To: John Williams, Construction Manager
         American Retail, Inc.
         123 Main St.
         City of Anywhere, CA, USA

Dear John and Others:
After reviewing the bid documents prepared by the architect and the design team dated 8/23/09, including construction drawings and specifications, addenda, notices, etc., and having visited the project site, we propose to provide materials, labor, equipment, and transportation to successfully construct the entire project called for in the bid documents as following:
   a. Base Bid: _____
       _____

       Note: All prices/costs shall be in both words and figures, and words shall prevail to prevent discrepancies.

   b. Breakdown:
       Major Building A: _____
       _____

       Site Work:_____
       _____

   c. Bond Premium

       Note: If awarded the contract, the undersigned bidder agrees to provide the owner a payment and performance equal to one hundred percent (100%) of the contract sum prior to the start of the construction and within 10 days of being awarded the contract.

       The base bid shall include the bond premium as listed here:_____
       _____

The owner reserves the right to obtain and pay for the bond separately and receive a bond premium as a credit back from the contractor.

d. Construction Schedule
The undersigned bidder agrees to start the construction within 1 week of receiving a written notice and complete the work within _____
_____calendar days.

e. Unit Price _____

f. Overhead and Profit: 10% for the base bid and any change orders.

g. Alternate (separate line item cost NOT included in the base bid): _____
_____

h. Separate Line Item Cost (included in the base bid): _____
_____

i. Addenda
The undersigned bidder certifies the receipt of the following notices and addenda and has included them in the base bid.

Major Building A	**Site Work**
Addendum A_____	Addendum A _____
Addendum B _____	Addendum B _____
Addendum C _____	Addendum C _____
Notice #1 _____	Notice #1 _____
Notice #2 _____	Notice #2 _____

j. Licenses: The undersigned bidder certifies s/he is a licensed contractor in the state where the project is located, and s/he will maintain the license for the duration of the project. The undersigned bidder certifies s/he will ONLY employ subcontractors who meet the license requirements in the state where the project is located.

k. The undersigned bidder certifies that s/he has read and understands the bid documents and is familiar with the type of the project s/he is bidding and the related codes, regulations, materials, and labor market, and has included allowances for contingencies. S/he has visited the site and investigated the site and the local condition.

l. Type of Firm _____
(Corporation, LLC, or Partnership, etc.)

Signature _____ Firm Seal _____

Print Name _____

Firm Name _____

Address _____

Tel _____

State Contractor License Number: _____

Signed on _____ Day of _____

Year of _____

Note: Each bidder shall return two sets of completed and signed bid proposal forms.

3. Instructions to Bidders: Major Issues to Cover:

The letter of instructions to all bidders includes a list of bid documents, definitions, procedures, tests, inspections and fees, payment and performance bond requirements, project schedule, soils report, and contract format.

Some items you may want to include in your instructions to bidders:

a. Bidders shall notify the architect of any <u>discrepancies</u> within the bid documents or between the bid documents and site condition immediately.
b. All questions from bidders (<u>RFIs</u>) shall be in writing and shall reach the architect no less than <u>8</u> days before the bid due date.
c. The bid shall be based on a <u>complete</u> set of bid documents. It is the bidder's responsibility to read and understand the complete set of bid documents.
d. Substitution requests shall be in writing and shall reach the architect no less than <u>11</u> days before the bid due date. The bidder shall be responsible for additional coordination and shall bear all additional costs related to substitution, including but not limited to design and testing costs, governing agency approval, etc.
e. All addenda will be sent out at least <u>5</u> days before the bid due date.
f. The owner has the right to <u>reject any and all bids</u>.
g. The owner has the right to <u>waive any irregularity and informality</u> in bid proposals received.
h. <u>No</u> bid can be <u>withdrawn</u> for <u>65</u> calendar days after the bid opening.
i. <u>Fees</u> for permits, testing, inspections, etc., shall be paid by the contractor and shall be included as part of the base bid.

j. Within 10 days of awarding the bid, the <u>successful bidder</u> shall submit a certificate of <u>insurance</u>, an executed payment and performance <u>bond</u>, a schedule of construction, cost breakdowns, a list of subcontractors, etc., to the architect.

4. Bid Tabulation Form

A **Bid Tabulation Form** is used to write down the summary of each bidder's proposal during the bid opening. The following is a sample bid tabulation form:

Table 6.2   Sample Bid Tabulation Form

Bid Tabulation Form for Major Building A for American Retail, Inc.
Located at City of Anywhere, CA, USA

A+A Job #: 09388   Date: 10/8/09

Bidder (firm name)	Base Bid	Bid Breakdown		Bond Pre-mium	Project Schedule	All Addenda & Notices rec'd?	Alternate Bid	Unit Price	Sep. Line Item Cost	Misc.	Remarks
		Major A	Site								
General Construc-tion, Inc. (bidder #1)											
Universal Builders, Inc. (bidder #2)											
Western Builders, Inc. (bidder #3)											

5. Distribution List

The **Distribution List** is a very important tool for project management. It helps you to keep track of who has got what from you. This is extremely valuable when disputes arise in the project.

The following is a sample distribution list:

Table 6.3   Sample Distribution List

Distribution List for Major Building A for American Retail, Inc.
Located at City of Anywhere, CA, USA

A+A Job #: 09388   Revised on 12/23/09

Name and Address	Bid Set issued on 9/8/09	Addendum A issued on 9/18/09	Addendum B issued on 9/28/09	Bid Award on 10/18/09	Bulletin 1 issued on 10/28/09	Bulletin 2 issued on 11/18/09
American Retail, Inc. (developer) 168 Broadway, Suite 108 City of Anywhere, CA Tel: 123-456-7890	1 set of ½ size & 1 spec. book	1 set of ½ size revised sheet, narrative of Add. A	1 set of ½ size revised sheet, narrative of Add. B		1 set of ½ size revised sheet, narrative of Bul. 1	1 set of ½ size revised sheet, narrative of Bul. 2
Best for Less, Inc. (tenant) 166 Broadway, Suite 118 City of Anywhere, CA Tel: 123-456-7890	Same as above	Same as above	Same as above		Same as above	Same as above
General Construction, Inc. (bidder #1) 118 Broadway, Suite 103 City of Anywhere, CA Tel: 123-456-7891	1 set of full size & 1 spec. book	1 set of full size revised sheet, narrative of Add. A	1 set of full size revised sheet, narrative of Add. B	Not selected		
Universal Builders, Inc. (bidder #2) 126 Main St., Suite B City of Anywhere, CA Tel: 123-456-7892	Same as above	Same as above	Same as above	Selected as **successful bidder**	1 set of full size revised sheet, narrative of Bul. 1	1 set of full size revised sheet, narrative of Bul. 2
Western Builders, Inc. (bidder #3) 138 First St., Suite B City of Anywhere, CA Tel: 123-456-7893	Same as above	Same as above	Same as above	Not selected		
A+A, Inc., (architect) 126 Main St., Suite B City of Anywhere, CA Tel: 123-456-7896	1 set of ½ size & 1 spec. book	1 set of ½ size revised sheet, narrative of Add. A	1 set of ½ size revised sheet, narrative of Add. B		1 set of ½ size revised sheet, narrative of Bul. 1	1 set of ½ size revised sheet, narrative of Bul. 2
CTS, Inc., (civil eng.) 168 Broadway, Suite 109 City of Anywhere, CA Tel: 123-456-7898	Same as above	Same as above	Same as above		Same as above	Same as above

Green Design, Inc., (land-scape architect) 118 Broadway, Suite 103 City of Anywhere, CA Tel: 123-456-7891	Same as above	Same as above	Same as above		Same as above	Same as above
ABF, Inc., (structural eng.) 126 Main St., Suite K City of Anywhere, CA Tel: 123-456-7892	Same as above	Same as above	Same as above		Same as above	Same as above
EGL, Inc., (electrical eng.) 138 First St., Suite L City of Anywhere, CA Tel: 123-456-7893	Same as above	Same as above	Same as above		Same as above	Same as above
MGI, Inc., (mechanical eng.) 1198 Broadway, Suite 106 City of Anywhere, CA Tel: 123-456-7895	Same as above	Same as above	Same as above		Same as above	Same as above
PCI, Inc., (plumbing eng.) 1128 Broadway, Suite 106 City of Anywhere, CA Tel: 123-456-7895	Same as above	Same as above	Same as above		Same as above	Same as above

Note: All contact information above is fictitious, for demonstration purposes only.

6. Document Control Sheet

The **Document Control Sheet** is also a very important tool for project management. It helps everyone to keep track of the latest sheets in the most current CD set. This is extremely valuable for effective communications.

You can send a document control sheet to the field, and the general contractor and ALL subcontractors can immediately find out if they have the most current sheets for the CD set. You do NOT have to repeatedly send out the complete CD set, and you can save a lot of paper (and many trees).

*Note: You ALWAYS need to keep ONE copy of the most current set of CD plans and specifications book in your architectural office. This is the full-size **original and CURRENT set** that you will use to make copies for everyone else if they need an extra current copy. This set can be placed in the flat file cabinet or rolled up and placed at a location near the project manager for this project.*

Every time you issue an addendum or bulletin, you HAVE to **replace** the old sheets in the original and CURRENT set with the revised sheets. You need to use a red pencil to cross out the lower right-hand corner of the old sheets and write down "Voided on (the date that the sheet was voided, for example, 9/8/09)." This is a very important step to differentiate the current sheets with the old sheets to avoid confusion.

The following is a sample document control sheet:

Table 6.4   Sample Document Control Sheet

Document Control Sheet for Major Building A for American Retail, Inc.
Located at City of Anywhere, CA, USA

A+A Job #: 09388   Revised on 12/23/09

Sheet No.	Sheet Title	Bid Set Date	Addendum A Date	Addendum B Date	Bid Award on 10/18/09	Bulletin 1 Date	Bulletin 2 Date
Architectural							
A0.0	Title Sheet	9/8/09	9/18/09				11/18/09
GN1.0	Accessibility Requirements	9/8/09				10/28/09	
GN2.0	General Notes	9/8/09		9/28/09			
AS1.0	Architectural Site Plan	9/8/09					11/18/09
A1.0	Floor Plan	9/8/09	9/18/09				11/18/09
A2.0	Reflected Ceiling Plan	9/8/09					11/18/09
A3.0	Roof Plan	9/8/09					11/18/09
A4.0	Exterior Elevations	9/8/09	9/18/09			10/28/09	
A5.0	Sections	9/8/09				10/28/09	
A6.0	Room, Door, and Window Schedules	9/8/09					
A7.0	Details	9/8/09					
A8.0	Details	9/8/09					
A9.0	Details	9/8/09					
A10.0	Hardscape Plans	9/8/09					
Structural							
ST1.0	General Notes and Details	9/8/09					
ST2.0	Framing Details	9/8/09					
ST3.0	Framing Details	9/8/09					
S1.0	Foundation Plans	9/8/09	9/18/09				11/18/09
S2.0	Framing Plans	9/8/09	9/18/09			10/28/09	11/18/09
S3.0	Sections	9/8/09				10/28/09	
S3.1	Sections	9/8/09					
Electrical							
E0.0	Electrical Notes & Details	9/8/09				10/28/09	
E0.1	Electrical Notes & Details	9/8/09					
E0.2	Electrical Title 24	9/8/09					
E1.0	Power Plans & Panel Schedules	9/8/09	9/18/09				11/18/09
E2.0	Lighting Plans	9/8/09	9/18/09				11/18/09

Mechanical							
M0.0	Equipment Schedules, Notes, and Details	9/8/09				10/28/09	
M1.0	Mechanical (or HVAC) Floor Plan and T-24 Energy Form	9/8/09					11/18/09
Plumbing							
P0.0	Plumbing Schedules, Notes, Legend, and Details	9/8/09				10/28/09	
P1.0	Plumbing Floor Plans	9/8/09	9/18/09				11/18/09

D. Pre-Bid Meeting & Pre-Bid Walk-Through

The **Pre-Bid Meeting** is a meeting for the owner, tenant, architect, and engineers to answer questions that bidders may have on the bid and the bid documents. **Pre-Bid Walk-Through** is a walk-through for the bidders to become familiar with the site and the scope of the work. The owner, tenant, architect, and engineers are often present at the walk-through. Pre-Bid Meeting & Pre-Bid Walk-Through can be organized together.

The timing for the Pre-Bid Meeting & Pre-Bid Walk-Through is important. For example, if you give the bidders a total of 4 weeks to bid the project, you probably want to set up the Pre-Bid Meeting & Pre-Bid Walk-Through 2 weeks after you issue the bid documents.

This way, the bidders have 2 weeks to review the bid documents, and when they come to the meeting and walk-through, they already have an understanding of the drawings and specifications and they can ask intelligent questions. In the meantime, you do not want to set the Pre-Bid Meeting & Pre-Bid Walk-Through too close to the bid due date, since the bidders may still have some questions after the meeting and walk-through.

Again, you need to draw a line somewhere and stop the bidders from asking questions (typically 8 days before the bid due date), so that you can have time to respond to their questions. Your last response to the bidders' RFIs shall be issued no later than 5 days before the bid due date. This way, all the bidders can have a level playfield and base their bid on exactly the same information and can focus on submitting a quality bid in the last few days before the bid due date.

Chapter Seven

Construction Administration

A. Construction Kick-Off Meeting

After the contract is awarded and before the construction starts, all parties related to the construction should attend the Construction Kick-Off Meeting. These parties include the developer's or owner's representative/construction manager (CM), tenant's CM, architect, engineers/consultants, general contractor, subcontractors, etc.

An architect may need to do a brief presentation in the meeting. The presentation package should include:

1. **Project Contact Information**

   It can be a simple contact list, including project number, name, address, the company's name, contact person, address, phone number, fax number, e-mail address for the construction lender, developer or owner, tenant, governing agencies (planning dept., building dept., health dept., inspector, etc.), utilities companies (gas, phone, cables, power, water, sewer, etc.), architect, engineers/consultants, general contractor, job site trailer, etc.

2. **Communication Protocol**

   a. All subcontractors' communication should go through the general contractor.
   b. All communication to the architect's consultants shall go through the architect.
   c. Group all the questions together and try to make a maximum of one or two daily calls to the architect.
   d. The verbal responses of the architect to RFI shall be confirmed in writing by the contractor.

3. **Construction Administration Procedure**

   a. **Dealing with Inspectors**

   Keep a good relationship with the inspector, but if he requests a change in the field, the contractor shall notify and get instructions from the architect first BEFORE making any change. Ask for the code section related to the requested change, the inspector's name, phone number, e-mail address, and information regarding the best time to call.

b. **Submittals**

Each submittal should have a proper letter of transmittal and should have been reviewed AND stamped by the general contractor BEFORE submitting to the architect for review. A minimum of <u>five</u> sets of submittals shall be sent to the architect.

Long lead-time items, such as steel and electrical switchgear, shall be submitted within 20 days of the award of the contract and definitely before the first payment request. Partial or incomplete submittals will NOT be reviewed and will be returned to the contractor without action. Allow at least 2 weeks for submittal reviews.

c. **Substitutions**

Some developers and owners will NOT allow substitutions. If that is the case, this should have been indicated in the contract documents.

When substitutions are allowed, the substitution requests shall be made during the bidding process or <u>within 30 days</u> of the award of the contract. The architect may back-charge the contractors for substitution requests made after the award of the contract for the extra time spent reviewing the substitutions.

It is the contractors' responsibilities to provide testing and guarantees to prove the substitutions will work equally as well or better than originally specified items and provide all necessary coordination related to the changes and bear any additional costs.

d. **Job Site Trailer Plans and "As-Built" Plans**

The contractor shall keep a current set of contract documents, including plans and spec., at the **job site trailer** and make them accessible for the architect and the developer's and tenant's construction manager.

The contractor shall keep a current set of plans and markup and update DAILY any actual installations that are substantially different from the plans. At the end of the job, this set of mark-up record plans, or **as-built plans,** shall be verified and signed by the contractor and each respective subcontractor on each sheet and forwarded to the architect.

e. **Quality Control**

The contractor shall pay for all tests and inspections required by the governing agencies and contract documents. S/he shall forward a copy of each test or inspection report to the governing agencies (if required), owner, architect, and related engineers. These reports shall be certified and signed by the testing lab's supervising engineer.

If any of these tests and inspections requires the architect's or engineer's observations, the contractor shall give at least 1 week of advanced notice.

f. **Payment Request**

The contractor shall use the standard **AIA Form G702, Application and Certification for Payment**, and **AIA Form G703, Continuation Sheet for G702**. The percentage of the payment shall be per approved payment schedule and based on the actual percentage of completion of the project as approved by the owner and the architect in monthly job site meetings.

The contractor can only include approved change orders as part of the payment request. S/he shall provide a **Conditional Lien Release** for any new payment requested and **Unconditional Lien Release** for previous payments already received from the owner.

The contractor shall certify that he has contacted all the materials and equipment suppliers and found out if any of them are **hard to obtain or have long lead-time** before the first payment request.

The contractor shall submit at least five copies of the payment request to the architect and send one copy to the owner simultaneously. The architect will review the payment request. If it is approved, then he will keep one copy for his file and send the remaining approved copies to the owner.

g. **A Brief Discussion of Other Construction-Related Items**

You can include a brief discussion of other construction-related items, such as Addendum and Bulletin, Request For Information (RFI) and RFI Log, Change Order (CO) and Change Order Log, Submittals & Submittal Log, Final Punch Walk and Punch List, Certificate of Substantial Completion, etc. You should request that the contractors maintain and update their own RFI Log, Change Order Log, and Submittal Log in a timely manner, at least on a weekly basis.

4. **This presentation is general in nature.** Nothing in it shall supersede the requirements of the contract documents.

B. Addendum and Bulletin

Addenda and bulletins are similar, but they are also different:

1. Both are used to issue changes to construction documents, including plans and specifications.
2. An addendum is used to issue revisions to construction documents AFTER bid documents are sent to the contractors, but BEFORE bids are turned in by the bidding con-

tractors. Normally, it should be issued at least 5 days BEFORE the bid due date to avoid confusion to the bidders. Revisions issued via an addendum have NO cost impact. So if a contractor submits a change order later based on revisions issued by an addendum, you can deny it because it should have already been included as part of the bid price.

3. Changes issued in an addendum should be **clouded** and **noted with a LETTER (within a Delta symbol)** and a date on the revision block of the sheet. For example, "Addendum A, 11/11/2009." This is easy to remember because changes issued in an addendum have **no cost impact**. They are noted with a LETTER. Do NOT note the revision ("Addendum A, 11/11/2008") on the title block of every sheet. ONLY note them on the title block of the revised sheets.

4. A bulletin is used to issue changes AFTER bid proposals are submitted by the bidding contractors and probably AFTER the contract is signed between the owner and the successful bidder. Revisions issued via a bulletin may have cost impact. They may qualify for change orders.

5. Changes issued in a bulletin should be **clouded** and **noted with a NUMBER (within a Delta symbol)** and a date on the revision block of the revised sheet. For example, "Bulletin #1, 12/18/2009." This is easy to remember because changes issued in a bulletin may have cost impact. They are noted with a NUMBER. Do NOT note the revision ("Bulletin #1, 12/18/2009") on the title block of every sheet. ONLY note them on the title block of the revised sheets.

6. The bulletin description shall include the language for the contractor to provide pricing per proposed changes and s/he shall proceed ONLY if the pricing is accepted by the client (the owner or the developer or the tenant, depending on whom the contractor has signed a contract with).

7. Both shall include the REVISED drawing sheets ONLY and sheet-by-sheet narrative of the changes for each revised sheet.

8. A typical addendum or bulletin shall include:

   a. A letter of transmittal listing all items sent with the addendum or bulletin
   b. REVISED drawings sheets ONLY, not the entire drawing set
   c. REVISED specifications sheets (if any) ONLY, not the entire specifications book
   d. A sheet-by-sheet narrative of the changes
   e. An updated Document Control Sheet

As long as you issue the **Document Control Sheet**, the contractors will know if they have the latest set, and there is no need to reissue the entire drawing set or the entire specifications book every time you issue an addendum or a bulletin. You can save a lot of paper (and trees) by using the document control sheet.

You and the contractor should each keep a **record set** of the **drawings** (the **"Stick Set"** or "Office Record Set." This is different from the full-size **original and CURRENT set** that you use to make extra current copies for others) and **specifications**.

I prefer to use a half-size set as a **"Stick Set"** because it takes much less space. This set shall have ALL the latest information. Each time an addendum or bulletin is issued, this set shall be updated. For example, if you have a REVISED Sheet A1.0, you should <u>fold</u> the lower right-hand corner of the <u>old</u> Sheet A1.0, <u>staple</u> the corner, and then insert the <u>new</u> and <u>REVISED</u> Sheet A1.0 <u>in front of</u> the <u>old</u> Sheet A1.0. This way, you easily track all the history of the changes.

You can file the 8½ x 11 portion of the addendum or bulletin revisions listed at item 7 above in your project folder.

It is a good idea to make an EXTRA copy of these <u>8½ x 11</u> pages and place them <u>on the front of</u> your office record set of the **specifications book**. You should use an Acon fastener or a thick three ring binder to hold your office record set of the specifications book. This way, you can easily add <u>8½ x 11</u> pages to the front of the binder and track all the history of the changes.

Each of these specifications books should be <u>clearly marked on the side</u> with the project number, name, and city so that it can be easily identified when placed on your bookshelf.

C. Request For Information (RFI) and RFI Log

At the beginning of the construction administration stage, the architect should set up the RFI log. See Table 7.1 as a sample. This is very important, and it will enable the architect to clearly track the status of each RFI at all times. The proper way to handle a RFI is:

1. When a RFI comes in, immediately log it in, or at least log it in on the same day that you receive it.
2. Look through the RFI and identify if it is for a consultant's review or your review. If a RFI is for a consultant's review, you need to forward it to that consultant right away since your consultant needs time to review the submittal. Please log in the date that you send out the RFI to the consultant.

   For example, site asphalt concrete paving, site waterlines, site fire sprinkler lines RFIs are for the **civil engineer's review.**

   Site irrigation and landscape submittals are for a **landscape architect's review.**

   RFIs related to concrete (concrete mix, grout, rebar), anchor bolt setting plans and footing types, structural steel columns, CMU, stonework, steel joists, metal decking, glulam beams, and prefabricated joists are for the **structural engineer's review.**

   The **fire sprinkler system** is typically <u>designed/built</u> by contractors. The <u>building</u> fire sprinkler RFI should be forwarded to the fire sprinkler consultant (typically hired by the owner or developer) and structural engineer for review. The structural engineer can double check if the structure can support the load for the fire sprinkler system, especially pipes with a diameter of 6" or larger.

Electrical RFIs for electrical equipment (switchgear, etc.), light fixtures, and the fire alarm are for the **electrical engineer's review.**

HVAC RFIs (RTU, ductwork, etc.) are for the **mechanical engineer's review.**

Plumbing RFIs are for the **plumbing engineer's review.**

3. Review your portions of the RFIs per the plans and specifications. These RFIs include: door and window, storefront, floor and wall finish, roofing and roof tiles (send them to the roofing consultant for review if your project has an independent roofing consultant hired by the owner), metal stud and drywalls (you may need to send the metal stud RFIs to the structural engineer for review), sheet metal, insulation, flashing and caulking, joint sealers, waterproofing, hardware, plaster, paint, toilet accessories, truncated domes, etc.

4. A common pitfall is that an architect does not update the RFI log or does not forward RFIs to consultants in a timely manner. A normal turnaround time for submittal is 5 to 10 working days. This is defined in your project's specifications.

5. NONE of the **bidding stage RFIs** (RFIs that are responded to BEFORE the bid due date) shall be a basis for change orders, since they should have been included in the bid already.

6. The **construction stage RFIs** (RFIs that are responded to AFTER the bid due date) may be a basis for change orders if they involved extra cost and the answers to them can NOT be found in your construction documents, i.e., plans and spec., or RFI responses during bidding process, etc.

You should be very careful when responding to these RFIs, and you should always try to refer your response to specific pages of plans and spec. whenever possible. If the responses to these RFIs can be found on the plans or in the spec. book, then these RFIs shall NOT qualify for change orders.

Table 7.1   Sample RFI Log

RFI Log for Major Building A for American Retail, Inc.
Located at City of Anywhere, CA, USA

A+A Job #: 09388   Revised on 12/23/09

RFI #	Description	A+A Architect Received on	Consultants		Other		Ret. To Contractor	Remark
			Sent	Rec'd	Sent	Rec'd		
Bidding Stage RFIs								
1	Multiple vendors and doors; which one?	4/25/08			Tenant-4/25/08	4/25/08	4/25/08	Either is OK but should be consistent.
2	FF=1561.50? CMU or conc. wall at dock? Use 4/A10 or 4/S1.0?	5/2/08					5/2/08	FF=1561.5. Use 4/S1.0
3	Ext. finishes per A4.0? 1" reveal? 3 coats or 2 coats?	5/5/08					5/5/08	
4	Spec. Div 11, 07239, 07322, split face CMU, 3/A-11-all not used?	5/4/08					5/5/08	Yes
5	Use OSB to substitute plywood	5/4/08					5/5/08	Only if OSB is not exposed to view.
6	Vases, F.S. line, SD line, parking, etc.	5/8/08					5/8/08	
Construction Stage RFIs								
7	Fire protection notes on T3.0; need dwg & data on tenant's racks.	7/7/08			To tenant on 7/10/08	7/15/08		Not available per tenant

8	Dim for col at stock room	7/11/08	ABF 7/11/08	7/11/08				7/11/08	It should be relocated to the corner near the CMU wall.
9	Disconnect & walker duct	7/13/08	EGL- 7/13/08	7/13/08				7/13/08	
9-re-sent	Disconnect & walker duct	Resent on 9/29/08						10/10/08	2nd response on 10/3/06 by the tenant
10	Relocated col. at the stock room area	7/13/08	ABF-7/13/08	7/14/08				7/17/08	
11	Existing conduits at footing?	7/17/08	ABF-7/17/08	7/18/08				7/18/08	
11A	How to correct front col. that was mista-kenly placed by the contractor?	7/18/08	ABF-7/18/08						
12	No cold joint at adja-cent footing?	7/17/08	ABF-7/17/08	7/18/08				7/18/08	
13	Beam to column (col) connection at grid A & 1.2	7/19/08	ABF-7/19/08					7/20/08	See 4/ST4
14	Move #4 from 40" to 32"?	7/21/08	ABF-7/21/08	7/24/08				7/24/08	OK
15	Smoke curtain loca-tion—move one bay?	7/26/08						7/31/08	OK
16	Various structural questions	7/31/08	ABF-7/31/08	7/31/08				7/31/08	OK
17	Clay tile lead time	8/7/08				Site archi-tect-8/7/08	8/7/08	8/7/08	
18	Rebar near grids A&1	8/10/08	ABF-8/10/08					8/10/08	

#	Description							
19	Arbor in foreground	8/10/08			Site architect- 8/10/08	9/21/08	9/22/08	
20	Walker duct dim & ext. fixture mounting ht?	8/15/08			Tenant & site architect- 8/15/08		9/8/08 for mounting ht	11'-11"
21	Need tenant equipment cut sheets	8/17/08	Tenant 8/17/08					
22	Walker duct sizing and dimension clarification for light fixtures	8/25/08	EGL 8/25/08				8/25/08	
23	P1 color change	8/25/08			Developer & site architect 8/25/08	Site architect 8/28/08	8/28/08	
24	The contractor missed anchor bolt in CMU and is asking about epoxy procedure.	8/31/08	ABF-9/1/08	9/6/08			9/6/08	
25	CMU wall above storefront	8/31/08	ABF-9/1/08	9/11/08			9/11/08	
26	Tile, etc., for sign by others?	8/31/08					9/11/08	Tile by building contractor
27	O.D. & R.D. discharge height	8/31/08					9/5/08	
28	Parapet braces height	9/5/08	ABF-9/5/08	9/6/08			9/6/08	Reduced from 10' to 5'; provide credit accordingly.
29	Rebar correction notice 2/ST2	9/12/08	ABF-9/12/08	9/13/08			9/14/08	OK
30	Connection at A5.0 & S3.0	9/14/08	ABF-9/14/08	9/14/08			9/14/08	
31	Cut slab for F.S. riser	9/22/08	ABF-9/22/08	9/22/08			9/22/08	

32	Need steel support for cut opening?	9/25/08	ABF-9/25/08				10/10/08	
33	Note 61, metal reveal	10/2/08						
34	OSB in lieu of plywood for vertical canopy wall, except sign backing location	10/2/08	10/2/08	10/9/08			10/9/08	
35	Substitute methods for slip track	10/4/08	ABF-10/4/08	10/9/08			10/9/08	
36	"J" box above 1-hr corridor	10/5/08	EGL-10/9/08				10/10/08	
37	Floor finish material in corridor 108	10/16/08			Tenant-10/16/08	10/16/08	10/16/08	
38	Elec RFI 6, 7 & 8	10/23/08	EGL-10/23/08	10/23/08			10/23/08	
38a	Further questions on TVSS	10/24/08	EGL-10/24/08				10/24/08	

Note: A+A is the architect, ABF is the structural engineer, MSI is the mechanical engineer, PBI is the plumbing engineer, and EGL is the electrical engineer.

D. CCD, Change Order (CO), and Change Order Log

A **Construction Change Directive (CCD)** is used when there are changes that do not involve extra cost and time or may involve minor extra cost and time and the project is on a tight schedule. Architects can issue a CCD to the contractor and instruct him to start the work per CCD. Use the standard AIA Form G714™-2007, Construction Change Directive, or make your own form for the CCD.

A **change order** covers the additional time or money for construction. It occurs when the scope of construction work changes AFTER the bid proposal is submitted and the contract is awarded. It can be a change requested by the owner, governing agencies, the tenant, or other parties. The change order caused by the tenant's request should be listed separately from other change orders, because it is a cost typically passed through to the tenant by the developer. The contractor can use **AIA standard form G701 Change Order.**

The contractor shall submit at least <u>five</u> copies of each change order to the architect. If a change order involves a consultant's work or a tenant' request, you (the architect) should forward it to the appropriate party for review first, and then review it yourself. If it is acceptable, you can approve it and then forward it to the owner for final approval.

You can make a **change order log** to list all the change orders for a project. It can be done in a format similar to a RFI log. It should include project number, name, address, etc. It should list all the change orders by change order number, and include description, reason of change, amount, date of receipt, date of forwarding to consultant or tenant for review, date of architect's approval, date of forwarding to the owner, and the date of final approval by the owner. It can be done on a spreadsheet format for easy accounting.

A contractor shall submit a change order request within 4 weeks of issuance of a bulletin. Overhead and profit is typically 10% for the contractor and subcontractors, but you need to check the actual percentage allowed by the spec. book.

The following is a sample **change order log**:

Table 7.2   Sample Change Order Log

Change Order (CO) Log for Major Building A for American Retail, Inc.
Located at City of Anywhere, CA, USA

A+A Job #: 09388   Rev. Date: 9/18/09

CO No.	Description	Amount	A+A Rec'd	Consultant Review		Other Review		A+A Approval	Owner Approval		Remarks
				Sent	Rec'd	Sent	Rec'd		Sent	Rec'd	
1	Add steel trellis	$5,500	1/2/09	1/2/09 to ABF	1/8/09	1/2/09 to tenant	1/19/09	1/19/09	1/19/09	1/28/09	
2	Change Kawneer storefront to Arcadia storefront	-$2,000 credit	1/3/09						1/3/09	1/28/09	

Note: A+A is the architect, ABF is the structural engineer, MSI is the mechanical engineer, PBI is the plumbing engineer, and EGL is the electrical engineer.

E.   Submittals: Shop Drawings, Product Data, and Samples

What to look for when reviewing submittals: Submittals include shop drawings, product data, and samples. At the beginning of the construction administration stage, the architect should set up the **submittal log**. See Table 7.3 as a sample. This is very important, and it will enable the architect to clearly track the status of each submittal at all times. The proper way to handle a submittal:

1. When a submittal comes in, immediately log it in, or at least log it in on the same day that you receive it.

2. Look through the submittal and identify if it is for a consultant's review or your review. If a submittal is for a consultant's review, you need to forward it to that consultant right away since your consultant needs time to review the submittal also. Please log in the date that you send out the submittal to the consultant.

   For example, site asphalt concrete paving, site waterlines, and site fire sprinkler lines submittals are for a **civil engineer's review.**

   Site irrigation and landscape submittals are for a **landscape architect's review.**

   Submittals related to concrete (concrete mix, grout, rebar), anchor bolt setting plans and footing types, structural steel columns, CMU, stonework, steel joists, glulam beams, and prefabricated joists are for the **structural engineer's review.** The structural engineer also reviews submittal for metal decking and metal studs. The structural plans should have a table for various gauges and sizes of metal studs required for certain heights. Ask your structural engineer to check the gauge and size of metal studs in the submittals to make sure they will work for the heights required.

   The building fire sprinkler system is typically designed/built by contractors. Fire sprinkler submittals should be forwarded to the structural engineer for review. The structural engineer can double check if the building structure can support the load for a fire sprinkler system, especially pipes with a diameter of 6" or larger.

   Electrical submittals, such as electrical equipment (switchgear, etc.), light fixtures, and fire alarms are for the **electrical engineer's review.**

   HVAC submittals (RTU, ductwork and related smoke detector, exhaust fans, supply and return registers, etc.) are for the **mechanical engineer's review.**

   Plumbing submittals (toilet fixtures, sinks, faucets, etc.) are for the **plumbing engineer's review.**

3. Review **your (or the architect's) portion of the submittals** per the plans and specifications. These submittals include: doors, frames and windows, storefront shop drawings, floor and wall finish, roofing and roof tiles (send them to the roofing consultant for review if your project has an independent roofing consultant hired by the owner), metal stud and drywalls (you also need to send the metal submittals to the structural engineer for review), sheet metal, insulation, flashing and caulking, joint sealers, waterproofing, hardware, plaster, paint, toilet accessories, FRP, truncated domes, etc.

4. A common pitfall is that an architect does not update the submittal log or forward submittals to consultants in a timely manner. A normal turnaround time for submittal is 2 weeks. This is defined in your project's specifications.

5. You are going to **take one of the five actions** on the submittals. Many architects make a shop drawing/submittal review stamp and include these five choices (you should check one of the choices):

   a. **Reviewed:** Select this choice when you have no markup on the submittals.

   Note: "Reviewed" is probably better than "Approved," since the contractor is required to build the building per plans and spec.

   The architect's <u>review</u> of the shop drawings and submittals is limited to checking the <u>general</u> compliance of the submittals to the design intent as shown in the plans and spec., <u>not</u> for checking quantity or dimensions or other details of the shop drawings and submittals, or quality control of the shop drawings and submittals, or construction procedures, etc., all of which shall remain as the contractors' responsibilities. Review of a portion of an assembly shall <u>not</u> be interpreted as the review of the entire assembly.

   *These are standard **disclaimers** and should be part of your submittal review stamp.*

   b. **Furnished as corrected:** Select this option when you do not have many markups and do not want to review the revised submittal again.

   c. **Revise and resubmit:** Select this option when you have numerous markups and want to review the revised submittal again to make sure the contractors pick up your markups.

   d. **Rejected and resubmit.**

   e. **Submit specified item:** Select this option when the contractor did not submit the required item per plans or spec.

6. If the contractor has to submit the same submittal (for example, Submittal #6) several times, you may want to number it with the same submittal number, but add a, b, c, d, etc., to it, i.e., Submittals 6a, 6b, 6c, 6d, etc. This will make it easier for you to track and retrieve the submittals later.

7. Tips for reviewing submittals:

   a. Do NOT check dimensions and quantity. This shall be done by the contractors.

   Exception: Check switchgears, elevators, and other large equipment to make sure they will fit into the space specified on the plans. This is because often, you may NOT have accurate information for these items when you developed the plans. This can be your last chance to coordinate them with your plans.

b. Architects shall only place the submittal review stamp on the architect's portion of the work, i.e., the railing, simple roof access ladder, etc.

c. Do NOT stamp on structural, electrical, mechanical, or plumbing submittals or any other submittals in your consultants' scope of work. They shall be reviewed by engineers or consultants and marked up or stamped by them.

d. Check to make sure the manufacturers and systems are per plans and spec.

e. Check door swing directions to make sure they match plans (right-hand doors, right-hand reverse doors, left-hand doors, left-hand reverse doors, etc.).

*Note: If you are standing outside a room facing the door to the room, the door hinge is on the right side, and the door opens into the room, this is a **right-hand door**. On the other hand, if the door hinge is on the right-hand side and the door opens outwards toward you, then this is a **right-hand reverse** door. Similarly, a left-hand door and a left-hand reverse door operates the same way except the door hinge is on the left side.*

f. Check fire protection plans and add a note that the fire sprinkler (F.S.) pipes are not to be supported by 2x purlins.

g. The general contractor (GC) should have reviewed, checked, and stamped all the submittals from his subcontractors BEFORE he forwarded them to you. If you receive any submittals without the GC's submittal stamp, you should return them (without any action) to the GC for his review and stamp first, and then have him resubmit to you for your review. You should communicate this very clearly to the GC at the beginning of the job, and it should be noted on your spec.

h. If contractors provide submittals that are not required by the contract documents, you can return them without any action.

i. Check submittals against the tenant's criteria. You should have already incorporated the tenant's criteria as part of your construction documents.

Table 7.3   **Sample Submittal Log**

Submittal Log for Major Building A for American Retail, Inc.
Located at City of Anywhere, CA, USA
A+A Job #: 09388   **Revised on 12/23/09**

Submittal Number	Description	A+A Architect Received On	Consultants Sent To	Rec'd	Returned To Contractor (GC)	REVIEWED	FURNISH AS CORRECTED	REVISE & RESUBMIT	REJECTED & RESUBMIT	SUBMIT SPECIFIED ITEM	Remarks
1	Concrete mix	6/30/08	ABF-6/30/08	7/5/08	7/5/08	x					
2	Mortar mix, rebar, grout mix, letter of cert.	7/12/08	ABF-7/12/08	7/17/08	7/17/08		x				
3	Anchor bolt via fax	7/11/08	ABF-7/11/08	7/12/08	7/12/08		x				
4	Anchor setting plan & footing type	7/12/08	ABF-7/12/08	7/17/08	7/17/08		x				
5	Struct. steel & misc. metal	7/24/08	ABF-7/24/08	7/26/08	7/26/08		x				
6	Mech. sub. (RTU & air dist.)	7/31/08	MSI-7/31/08	8/2/08	8/2/08				x		
6a	Mech sub. (RTU & air dist.)	8/9/08	MSI-8/9/08	9/5/08	9/5/08		x				
6a1	Duct liner		MSI-9/6/08 sent by sub directly	9/7/08	9/7/08		x				
6a2	Smoke detector		MSI-9/6/08 sent by sub directly	9/7/08	9/7/08				x		

No.	Description					clay tile	built-up				Remarks
6b	Smoke detector, duct liner, air balance, and air outlets	9/11/08	MSI-9/11/08	9/20/08	9/20/08					X	Smoke detector is rejected; duct liner & air distribution are approved.
6c	Fan	9/18/08	MSI-9/18/08	9/20/08	9/20/08	X					
7	Clay roof tile & built-up roofing	8/2/08			8/2/08						
8	Elec. equip. & fixture	8/2/08	EGL elec.-8/2/08	8/7/08	8/7/08						
9	Metal stud/drywall	8/7/08			8/10/08	x					
10	Arch sheet metal	8/7/08			8/10/08		x				
10a	Arch sheet metal resubmittal	9/11/08			9/15/08		x				
11	Roof structural shop dwg & bill of mat.	8/7/08	ABF-8/7/08	8/10/08	8/10/08		x				
12	F.S. design & calcs.	8/7/08	ABF-8/7/08	8/10/08	8/10/08	x					
12a	F.S. design & calcs.	9/7/08	ABF-9/7/08	9/11/08	9/11/2008 resent on 9/20/06		x				
13	Hardware	8/7/08			8/10/08		x				
15	Paint sub.	8/9/08			8/10/08				x		
15a	Paint resubmittal	9/8/08			9/11/2008 resent on 9/20/08		x				

No.	Item	Date	Eng. Date	Date	Date	A+A	ABF	MSI	PBI	EGL	Remarks
15b	Paint resubmittal	9/14/08			9/15/08		x				Need P2 brush out
15c	Paint resubmittal	10/2/08			10/10/08	x					
16	Joint sealer	8/11/08			8/15/08		x				
17	Door & frame schedule	8/14/08			8/15/08		x				
18	Plumbing sub		PBI-8/15/08	8/22/08	8/22/08	x					
19	Fire alarm	9/1/08	EGL elec.-9/5/08	9/7/08	9/7/08				x		Not the correct vendor
19a	Fire alarm resubmittal	10/2/08	EGL elec.-10/2/08	10/13/08	10/16/08	x					
20	Concrete mix design for dock paving	9/14/08	ABF-9/14/08	9/18/08	9/18/08	X					
21	Insulation	9/14/08			9/15/08		x				
22	FRP samples & brochure	9/21/08			9/22/08				x		Use tenant-preferred vendor #29 per spec.
22a	FRP samples & brochure resubmittal	10/2/08			10/10/08		x				
23	Ladder sub	9/21/08	ABF-9/21/08	9/25/08	9/25/08		x				
23a	Roof joist shop drawings	10/13/08	ABF-10/16/08	10/18/08	10/19/08	x					

Note: *A+A is the architect, ABF is the structural engineer, MSI is the mechanical engineer, PBI is the plumbing engineer, and EGL is the electrical engineer.*

F. Field Observation

Per **AIA Form A201, General Conditions of the Contract for Construction**, an architect is not required to do exhaustive field visits but only needs to do periodic visits. These visits are field observation only, not field supervision.

However, if you do observe something that is done wrong in the field, you need to inform the owner in writing.

You should write a **field observation report** for each field visit. A field observation report needs to include:

1. Project **identification information,** such as project number, name, address, etc.
2. The **weather** condition and **date** of the visit.
3. Names, phone numbers, e-mails and mailing addresses of parties that attended the field observation. Typically, the **attendees** include the architect, the contractor's job site superintendent, and sometimes the owner's or the tenant's construction manager.
4. Description of percentage of completion:

   a. **Bottom Surfaces/Groundwork:** grading and excavation, footings, underground (U.G.) plumbing, like sewer and waterlines, U.G. electrical-like walker ducts, U.G. refrigeration, floor slab and related base, floor finishes, A.C. paving, sidewalk, irrigation lines, and landscape.
   b. **Vertical Work:** exterior walls and related insulation, exterior finish and veneers, interior walls and finish (painting, FRP, etc.), drywalls, doorframes and doors, windows and frames, hardware, storefront, columns, fixture, etc.
   c. **Top Surfaces:** roof framing, roofing and insulation, skylights (if any), fire sprinklers and related plumbing lines, ceiling (drywall ceiling, T-bar ceiling, etc.), lighting, HVAC registers, rooftop HVAC units (RTU), and condensation lines.
   d. **Other Trades:** electrical, plumbing, and mechanical items

5. Description of **materials stocked** at the site
6. List of the **subcontractors** working at the site
7. Note if the **percentage of completion** matches the construction schedule.
8. Confirmation of all **verbal instructions** given at the site.
9. Note if the **job site trailer set of plans** is well maintained and up-to-date.
10. Inform contractors of **upcoming revisions**, if any.
11. **Photos** taken at the visit

G. Final Punch Walk and Punch List

A **Final Punch Walk** is a final walk-through of the project by the architect or the owner's construction manager, often accompanied by the contractor's superintendent. The purpose of the walk is to check the building and the related site to make sure the project has been built per the construction documents (plans and spec. and all the addenda and bulletins, etc.).

A final punch walk should be performed after the contractors have done everything they can to finish the project per the construction documents; i.e., typically after the substantial completion.

A **Final Punch List** is a list of the items that the architect's or the owner's construction manager found on the project that shall be finished or corrected to match the construction documents. The items on the punch list shall be typically finished within 30 days. You should actually note this on the punch list.

Notes typically included on a punch list:

1. Contractors shall **correct all items** on the punch list before the project can be accepted.
2. The punch list **does NOT release** the contractor from complying with the requirements of the construction documents.
3. The items shall be finished/corrected within **30 days** of the date of the issuance of the punch list.
4. If the contractor does not correct the items in a timely manner, the owner has **the right to correct** the items and then deduct the cost from payment due to the contractor.
5. The contractor is to provide all **guarantees, operations instructions, and manuals** for all equipment.
6. The contractor shall provide a set of **"as-built" plans** before final payment.
7. The contractor shall provide an itemized accounting list for **actual uses** of the cash allowance.
8. The architect will list all items to be corrected by the contractor and noticed on the final walk by the architect.

   Items often missed by the contractors *include missing expansion joints, drip edges, fog coats for A.C. paving, splash blocks, paint on pipe guards, paint on switchgear, weather strips at exterior doors, sealant at pipe penetrations, sealant for storefront, lead counterflashing for vent pipes, electrical panel labeling, concrete sealer, FRP at toilet rooms and janitor's room, etc.*

H. Certificate of Substantial Completion

You can use the standard AIA Form G704 ™ Certificate of Substantial Completion, or you can create your own form. Include some basic language and information such as the following:

1. You can do this as a letter to the developer and include the developer's company name, contact name, address, and date.

2. Project name, address, and project number
3. Your signature, a list of enclosed items, and a cc list
4. "Based on our field observations and communications with the contractor, we find the project substantially completed per the contract documents."
5. A Certificate of Substantial Completion form establishes the date of Substantial Completion. This date has significant implications and is often the kick-off date of the warranty for the equipment, etc.
6. A Certificate of Substantial Completion often refers to the punch list and the time allowed to complete the punch list items, and the date that the owner will occupy the building or a portion thereof, and describes the responsibilities regarding insurance, utilities, heat, and maintenance.

Chapter Eight

Collections

Collection is a subject that people hate to discuss, but it is an important part of any business. You are in the business to make money, and you need to be able to collect your fees to stay in business.

A. Structure Your Contract to Make It Easier for You to Collect Your Fees

You may be using the AIA standard form, but make sure you structure your contract to make it easier for you to collect your fees. For example, you need to make sure your contract states that your client needs to pay you promptly when each phase of the work is completed. If a client does not pay, you have the right to stop working by giving him/her a 1-week advanced written notice, and you shall NOT be liable for any damages cause by stopping the work. Your design fees shall NOT be pending on your client's funding or financing of the project

Some architects place an interest clause for late payment. They may charge <u>1%</u> interest <u>per month</u> for late payments. Check your local laws and make sure your interest clause meets the requirements of your local laws and codes. This clause will give your client <u>an incentive to pay on time</u>.

For the client that you have never previously worked with, you may want to consider getting a certain percentage (<u>20%</u> typically) of your fees in advance as a **retainer** before you do any work for them.

B. What Should You Do if Your Client Is Late in Paying You?

You probably should have someone else, such as your staff in the accounting department, do the collection. This is for two reasons:

1. You still need to deal with the client in the future, and you may still want to get more projects from him/her.

2. A separate collection staff can also show your client that you are serious about collecting.

If the payment is late, find out from the client and your team why that is so. Do you have a signed contract or a signed **additional service request** for additional work? Has work been done properly and with quality? Are there any other issues that may have caused the late payment?

This is why it is a good idea <u>NOT</u> to do any work without the client's <u>written</u> authorization. If you have a <u>written</u> authorization, it will be much easier to collect the money.

If you check all the above and find no valid reason for the late payment, then you can do the following:

If the payment is <u>4 weeks</u> late, your collection staff should send your client <u>a letter</u> with another copy of the unpaid invoice and mark or stamp it as "<u>Second Notice</u>" to remind your client to pay.

If the payment is <u>6</u> weeks late, your collection staff should send your client <u>a second letter</u> in a more serious tone and ask the client, again, why the payment has not been paid. S/he can also attach another copy of the unpaid invoice and mark or stamp it as "<u>Third Notice</u>" to remind your client to pay.

Again, your design fees shall <u>NOT</u> be pending on your client's funding or financing of the project. It is not a valid reason if your client does not have money to pay you. S/he should <u>not</u> have asked for the design service if s/he did not have sufficient funds to pay you.

If the payment is <u>8</u> weeks late, your collection staff should send your client <u>another letter</u> and advise your client that your firm will <u>stop working</u> on the project if the payment is not received in 1 week.

If the payment is <u>12</u> weeks late, your collection staff should send your client <u>the fourth letter</u> and advise the client that your firm will either send the client to a <u>collection agency</u> or take <u>legal action</u> to collect the money.

If you have to send out <u>the fourth letter</u>, you will probably lose this client.

Well, why do you need a client who will not pay you for your service?

Appendixes

1. List of Tables

2. Definition of Architects and Some Important Information about Architects and the Profession of Architecture

Architects, Except Landscape and Naval

- Nature of the Work
- Training, Other Qualifications, and Advancement
- Employment
- Job Outlook
- Projections Data
- Earnings
- OES Data
- Related Occupations
- Sources of Additional Information

Significant Points

- About 1 in 5 architects are self-employed—more than 2 times the proportion for all occupations.
- Licensing requirements include a professional degree in architecture, at least 3 years of practical work training, and passing all divisions of the Architect Registration Examination.
- Architecture graduates may face competition, especially for jobs in the most prestigious firms.

Nature of the Work

People need places in which to live, work, play, learn, worship, meet, govern, shop, and eat. These places may be private or public; indoors or out; rooms, buildings, or complexes, and architects design them. Architects are licensed professionals trained in the art and science of building design who develop the concepts for structures and turn those concepts into images and plans.

Architects create the overall aesthetic and look of buildings and other structures, but the design of a building involves far more than its appearance. Buildings also must be functional, safe, and economical and must suit the needs of the people who use them. Architects consider all these factors when they design buildings and other structures.

Architects may be involved in all phases of a construction project, from the initial discussion with the client through the entire construction process. Their duties require specific skills—designing, engineering, managing, supervising, and communicating with clients and builders. Architects spend a great deal of time explaining their ideas to clients, construction contractors, and others. Successful architects must be able to communicate their unique vision persuasively.

The architect and client discuss the objectives, requirements, and budget of a project. In some cases, architects provide various pre-design services: conducting feasibility and environmental impact studies, selecting a site, preparing cost analysis and land-use studies, or specifying the requirements the design must meet. For example, they may determine space requirements by researching the numbers and types of potential users of a building. The architect then prepares drawings and a report presenting ideas for the client to review.

After discussing and agreeing on the initial proposal, architects develop final construction plans that show the building's appearance and details for its construction. Accompanying these plans are drawings of the structural system; air-conditioning, heating, and ventilating systems; electrical systems; communications systems; plumbing; and, possibly, site and landscape plans. The plans also specify the building materials and, in some cases, the interior furnishings. In developing designs, architects follow building codes, zoning laws, fire regulations, and other ordinances, such as those requiring easy access by people who are disabled. Computer-aided design and drafting (CADD) and Building Information Modeling (BIM) technology has replaced traditional paper and pencil as the most common method for creating design and construction drawings. Continual revision of plans on the basis of client needs and budget constraints is often necessary.

Architects may also assist clients in obtaining construction bids, selecting contractors, and negotiating construction contracts. As construction proceeds, they may visit building sites to make sure that contractors follow the design, adhere to the schedule, use the specified materials, and meet work quality standards. The job is not complete until all construction is finished, required tests are conducted, and construction costs are paid. Sometimes, architects also provide post-construction services, such as facilities management. They advise on energy efficiency measures, evaluate how well the building design adapts to the needs of occupants, and make necessary improvements.

Often working with engineers, urban planners, interior designers, landscape architects, and other professionals, architects in fact spend a great deal of their time coordinating information from, and the work of, other professionals engaged in the same project.

They design a wide variety of buildings, such as office and apartment buildings, schools, churches, factories, hospitals, houses, and airport terminals. They also design complexes such as urban centers, college campuses, industrial parks, and entire communities.

Architects sometimes specialize in one phase of work. Some specialize in the design of one type of building—for example, hospitals, schools, or housing. Others focus on planning and pre-design services or construction management and do minimal design work.

Work environment. Usually working in a comfortable environment, architects spend most of their time in offices consulting with clients, developing reports and drawings, and working with other architects and engineers. However, they often visit construction sites to review the progress of projects. Although most architects work approximately 40 hours per week, they often have to work nights and weekends to meet deadlines.

Training, Other Qualifications, and Advancement

There are three main steps in becoming an architect. First is the attainment of a professional degree in architecture. Second is work experience through an internship, and third is licensure through the passing of the Architect Registration Exam.

Education and training. In most States, the professional degree in architecture must be from one of the 114 schools of architecture that have degree programs accredited by the National Architectural Accrediting Board. However, State architectural registration boards set their own standards, so graduation from a non-accredited program may meet the educational requirement for licensing in a few States.

Three types of professional degrees in architecture are available: a 5-year bachelor's degree, which is most common and is intended for students with no previous architectural training; a 2-year master's degree for students with an undergraduate degree in architecture or a related area; and a 3- or 4-year master's degree for students with a degree in another discipline.

The choice of degree depends on preference and educational background. Prospective architecture students should consider the options before committing to a program. For example, although the 5-year bachelor of architecture offers the fastest route to the professional degree, courses are specialized, and if the student does not complete the program, transferring to a program in another discipline may be difficult. A typical program includes courses in architectural history and theory, building design with an emphasis on CADD, structures, technology, construction methods, professional practice, math, physical sciences, and liberal arts. Central to most architectural programs is the design studio, where students apply the skills and concepts learned in the classroom, creating drawings and three-dimensional models of their designs.

Many schools of architecture also offer post-professional degrees for those who already have a bachelor's or master's degree in architecture or other areas. Although graduate education beyond the professional degree is not required for practicing architects, it may be required for research, teaching, and certain specialties.

All State architectural registration boards require architecture graduates to complete a training period—usually at least 3 years—before they may sit for the licensing exam. Every State, with the exception of Arizona, has adopted the training standards established by the Intern Development Program, a branch of the American Institute of Architects and the National Council of Architectural Registration Boards (NCARB). These standards stipulate broad training under the supervision of a licensed architect. Most new graduates complete their training period by working as interns at architectural firms. Some States allow a portion of the training to occur in the offices of related professionals, such as engineers or general contractors. Architecture students who complete internships while still in school can count some of that time toward the 3-year training period.

Interns in architectural firms may assist in the design of one part of a project, help prepare architectural documents or drawings, build models, or prepare construction drawings on CADD. Interns also may research building codes and materials or write specifications for building materials, installation criteria, the quality of finishes, and other, related details.

Licensure. All States and the District of Columbia require individuals to be licensed (registered) before they may call themselves architects and contract to provide architectural services. During the time between graduation and becoming licensed, architecture school graduates generally work in the field under the supervision of a licensed architect who takes legal responsibility for all work. Licensing requirements include a professional degree in architecture, a period of practical training or internship, and a passing score on all divisions of the Architect Registration Examination. The examination is broken into nine divisions consisting of either multiple choice or graphical questions. The eligibility period for completion of all divisions of the exam varies by State.

Most States also require some form of continuing education to maintain a license, and many others are expected to adopt mandatory continuing education. Requirements vary by State but usually involve the completion of a certain number of credits annually or biennially through workshops, formal university classes, conferences, self-study courses, or other sources.

Other qualifications. Architects must be able to communicate their ideas visually to their clients. Artistic and drawing ability is helpful, but not essential, to such communication. More important are a visual orientation and the ability to understand spatial relationships. Other important qualities for anyone interested in becoming an architect are creativity and the ability to work independently and as part of a team. Computer skills are also required for writing specifications, for 2- and 3- dimensional drafting using CADD programs, and for financial management.

Certification and advancement. A growing number of architects voluntarily seek certification by the National Council of Architectural Registration Boards. Certification is awarded after independent verification of the candidate's educational transcripts, employment record, and professional references. Certification can make it easier to become licensed across States. In fact, it is the primary requirement for reciprocity of licensing among State Boards that are NCARB members. In 2007, approximately one-third of all licensed architects had this certification.

After becoming licensed and gaining experience, architects take on increasingly responsible duties, eventually managing entire projects. In large firms, architects may advance to supervisory or managerial positions. Some architects become partners in established firms, while others set up their own practices. Some graduates with degrees in architecture also enter related fields, such as graphic, interior, or industrial design; urban planning; real estate development; civil engineering; and construction management.

Employment

Architects held about 132,000 jobs in 2006. Approximately 7 out of 10 jobs were in the architectural, engineering, and related services industry—mostly in architectural firms with fewer than five workers. A small number worked for residential and nonresidential building construction firms and for government agencies responsible for housing, community planning, or construction of government buildings, such as the U.S. Departments of Defense and Interior, and the General Services Administration. About 1 in 5 architects are self-employed.

Job Outlook

Employment of architects is expected to grow faster than the average for all occupations through 2016. Keen competition is expected for positions at the most prestigious firms, and opportunities will be best for those architects who are able to distinguish themselves with their creativity.

Employment change. Employment of architects is expected to grow by 18 percent between 2006 and 2016, which is <u>faster than the average</u> for all occupations. Employment of architects is strongly tied to the activity of the construction industry. Strong growth is expected to come from nonresidential construction as demand for commercial space increases. Residential construction, buoyed by low interest rates, is also expected to grow as more people become homeowners. If interest rates rise significantly, home building may fall off, but residential construction makes up only a small part of architects' work.

Current demographic trends also support an increase in demand for architects. As the population of Sunbelt States continues to grow, the people living there will need new places to live and work. As the population continues to live longer and baby-boomers begin to retire, there will be a need for more healthcare facilities, nursing homes, and retirement communities. In education, buildings at all levels are getting older and class sizes are getting larger. This will require many school districts and universities to build new facilities and renovate existing ones.

In recent years, some architecture firms have outsourced the drafting of construction documents and basic design for large-scale commercial and residential projects to architecture firms overseas. This trend is expected to continue and may have a negative impact on employment growth for lower level architects and interns who would normally gain experience by producing these drawings.

Job prospects. Besides employment growth, additional job openings will arise from the need to replace the many architects who are nearing retirement, and others who transfer to other occupations or stop working for other reasons. Internship opportunities for new architectural students are expected to be good over the next decade, but more students are graduating with architectural degrees and some competition for entry-level jobs can be anticipated. Competition will be especially keen for jobs at the most prestigious architectural firms as prospective architects try to build their reputation. Prospective architects who have had internships while in school will have an advantage in obtaining intern positions after graduation. Opportunities will be best for those architects that are able to distinguish themselves from others with their creativity.

Prospects will also be favorable for architects with knowledge of "green" design. Green design, also known as sustainable design, emphasizes energy efficiency, renewable resources such as energy and water, waste reduction, and environmentally friendly design, specifications, and materials. Rising energy costs and increased concern about the environment has led to many new buildings being built green.

Some types of construction are sensitive to cyclical changes in the economy. Architects seeking design projects for office and retail construction will face especially strong competition for jobs or clients during recessions, and layoffs may ensue in less successful firms. Those involved in the design of institutional buildings, such as schools, hospitals, nursing homes, and correctional facilities, will be less affected by fluctuations in the economy. Residential construction makes up a small portion of work for architects, so major changes in the housing market would not be as significant as fluctuations in the nonresidential market.

Despite good overall job opportunities, some architects may not fare as well as others. The profession is geographically sensitive, and some parts of the Nation may have fewer new building projects. Also, many firms specialize in specific buildings, such as hospitals or office towers, and demand for these buildings may vary by region. Architects may find it increasingly necessary to gain reciprocity in order to compete for the best jobs and projects in other States.

Projections Data

Projections data from the National Employment Matrix

Occupational title	SOC Code	Employment, 2006	Projected employment, 2016	Change, 2006-16		Detailed statistics
				Number	Percent	
Architects, except landscape and naval	17-1011	132,000	155,000	23,000	18	PDF zipped XLS

NOTE: Data in this table are rounded. See the discussion of the employment projections table in the *Handbook* introductory chapter on *Occupational Information Included in the Handbook*.

Earnings

Median annual earnings of wage-and-salary architects were $64,150 in May 2006. The middle 50 percent earned between $49,780 and $83,450. The lowest 10 percent earned less than $39,420, and the highest 10 percent earned more than $104,970. Those just starting their internships can expect to earn considerably less.

Earnings of partners in established architectural firms may fluctuate because of changing business conditions. Some architects may have difficulty establishing their own practices and may go through a period when their expenses are greater than their income, requiring substantial financial resources.

Many firms pay tuition and fees toward continuing education requirements for their employees.

For the latest wage information:
The above wage data are from the Occupational Employment Statistics (OES) survey program, unless otherwise noted. For the latest National, State, and local earnings data, visit the following pages:

Architects, except landscape and naval

Related Occupations

Architects design buildings and related structures. Construction managers, like architects, also plan and coordinate activities concerned with the construction and maintenance of buildings and facilities. Others who engage in similar work are landscape architects, civil engineers, urban and regional planners, and designers, including interior designers, commercial and industrial designers, and graphic designers.

Sources of Additional Information

Disclaimer:
Links to non-BLS Internet sites are provided for your convenience and do not constitute an endorsement.

Information about education and careers in architecture can be obtained from:

- The American Institute of Architects, 1735 New York Ave. NW., Washington, DC 20006. Internet: http://www.aia.org
- Intern Development Program, National Council of Architectural Registration Boards, Suite 1100K, 1801 K St. NW., Washington, D.C. 20006. Internet: http://www.ncarb.org OOH ONET Codes 17-1011.00"

Quoted from: Bureau of Labor Statistics, U.S. Department of Labor, Occupational Outlook Handbook, 2008-09 Edition, Architects, Except Landscape and Naval, on the Internet at **http://www.bls.gov/oco/ocos038.htm** (visited November 30, 2008).
Last Modified Date: December 18, 2007

Note: Please check the website above for the latest information.

3. AIA Compensation Survey

Every 3 years, AIA publishes a Compensation Survey for various positions at architectural firms across the country. It is a good idea to find out the salary before you make the final decision to become an architect. If you are already an architect, it is also a good idea to determine if you are underpaid or overpaid.

See the link below for some sample pages for the 2008 AIA Compensation Survey:

http://www.aia.org/aiaucmp/groups/ek_public/documents/pdf/aiap072881.pdf

4. So ... You would Like to Study Architecture

To study architecture, you need to learn how to draft, how to understand and organize spaces and the interactions between interior and exterior spaces, how to do design, and how to communicate effectively. You also need to understand the history of architecture.

As an architect, a leader for a team of various design professionals, you not only need to know architecture, but also need to understand enough of your consultants' work to be able to coordinate them. Your consultants include soils and civil engineers, landscape architects, structural, electrical, mechanical, and plumbing engineers, interior designers, sign consultants, etc.

There are two major career paths for you in architecture: practice as an architect or teach in colleges or universities. The earlier you determine which path you are going to take, the more likely you will be successful at an early age. Some famous and well-respected architects, like my USC alumnus Frank Gehry, have combined the two paths successfully. They teach at the universities and have their own architectural practice. Even as a college or university professor, people respect you more if you have actual working experience and have some built projects. If you only teach in colleges or universities but have no actual working experience and have no built projects, people will consider you as a "paper" architect, and they are not likely to take you seriously, because they will think you probably do not know how to put a real building together.

In the U.S., if you want to practice architecture, you need to obtain an architect's license. It requires a combination of passing scores on the Architectural Registration Exam (ARE) and 8 years of education and/or qualified working experience, including at least 1 year of working experience in the U.S. Your working experience needs to be under the supervision of a licensed architect to be counted as qualified working experience for your architect's license.

If you work for a landscape architect or civil engineer or structural engineer, some states' architectural licensing boards will count your experience at a discounted rate for the qualification of your architect's license. For example, 2 years of experience working for a civil engineer may be counted as 1 year of qualified experience for your architect's license. You need to contact your state's architectural licensing board for specific licensing requirements for your state.

If you want to teach in colleges or universities, you probably want to obtain a master's degree or a Ph.D. It is not very common for people in the architectural field to have a Ph.D. One reason is that there are few Ph.D. programs for architecture. Another reason is that architecture is considered a profession and requires a license. Many people think an architect's license is more important than a Ph.D. degree. In many states, you need to have an architect's license to even use the title "architect," or the terms "architectural" or "architecture" to advertise your service. You cannot call yourself an architect if you do not have an architect's license, even if you have a Ph.D. in architecture. Violation of these rules brings punishment.

To become a tenured professor, you need to have a certain number of publications and pass the evaluation for the tenure position. Publications are very important for tenure track positions. Some people say for the tenured track positions in universities and colleges, it is "publish or perish."

The American Institute of Architects (AIA) is the national organization for the architectural profession. Membership is voluntary. There are different levels of AIA membership. Only licensed architects can be (full) AIA members. If you are an architectural student or an intern but not a licensed architect yet, you can join as an associate AIA member. Contact AIA for detailed information.

The National Council of Architectural Registration Boards (NCARB) is a nonprofit federation of architectural licensing boards. It has some very useful programs, such as IDP, to assist you in obtaining your architect's license. Contact NCARB for detailed information.

5. Annotated Bibliography

American Institute of Steel Construction. *Steel Construction Manual, 13th Edition.* American Institute of Steel Construction. 2006. This is a very expensive but also very valuable book for both architects and structural engineers. For architects, you can use this book to look up the sectional dimensions for columns and beams and their structural weight per linear foot, and then you can find out if your columns will fit inside an interior partition or find out the height of the beams. Then you can subtract the beam height, mechanical duct height, and T-bar ceiling height and floor thickness to calculate the actual ceiling heights for space under a mezzanine, etc.

Awad, Oussa. Editor-in-Chief. *California Accessibility Reference Manual Code & Checklist (CARM).* Builder's Book, Inc. 2009. For California, Title 24 has a set of accessibility regulations, which is not exactly the same as the federal ADA provisions. CARM blends California's accessibility regulations with federal ADA provisions and sorts out and explains the differences between the ADA & Title 24 that all California professionals must understand and follow to comply with both laws. CARM has more than 50 tables, 800 unique line drawings, and cross-referencing to the ADA and California's Title 24.

Ching, Francis. *Architecture: Form, Space, & Order.* Wiley, 2007. It is one of the best architectural books that you can have. I still flip through it every now and then. It is a great book for inspiration.

Ching, Francis. Steven R. Winkel, FAIA, PE. *Building Codes Illustrated: A Guide to Understanding the 2006 International Building Code.* Wiley, 2006. A valuable interpretive guide with many useful line drawings. A great timesaver.

Ching, Francis. *Building Construction Illustrated.* Wiley, 2008. The illustrations are great! Ching has a great talent to simplify complicated issues and make them very easy to understand.

Gibbens, Michael P. *California Disabled Accessibility Guidebook (CalDAG).* International Code Council, 2009. For California, Title 24 has a set of accessibility regulations, which is not exactly the same as the federal ADA provisions. CalDAG blends California's accessibility regulations with federal ADA provisions and sorts out and explains the differences between the ADA & Title 24 that all California professionals must understand and follow to comply with both laws. CalDAG has 14 flow charts, 250 computer-generated details, and complete checklists.

International Code Council. *2006 International Building Code—Softcover Version (International Building Code) (Paperback).* Delmar Cengage Learning, 2006. It is the model code adapted by 48 states in the U.S. as the building code.

Jellicoe, Geoffrey Alan. *The Landscape of Man: Shaping the Environment from Prehistory to the Present Day.* Thames & Hudson, 1995. Included are 28 sections that are separated into two parts. It contains 408 pages, 746 illustrations, and 6 maps. It is a great book for architects, landscape architects, and urban planners!

Morris, A. E. J. *History of Urban Form: Before the Industrial Revolution.* Prentice Hall, 1996. This book contains many great line drawings to illustrate city and urban planning and architecture in many different cultures throughout history. It enlightens you and encourages you to look at the design issue on a grand scale. With very powerful images, it shows the brilliance of human beings.

Ramsey, Charles George, and John Ray Hoke Jr. *Architectural Graphic Standards, Tenth Edition.* Wiley, 2000. It is organized roughly per the CSI MasterFormat divisions, including general planning and design data, site work, concrete, masonry, metals, wood, thermal and moisture protection, doors and windows, finishes, specialties, equipment, furnishings, special construction, conveying systems, mechanical, electrical, sports, energy, history preservation, etc.

Back Page Promotion

You may be interested in some other books written by Gang Chen:

1. *Planting Design Illustrated*
   http://outskirtspress.com/agent.php?key=11011&page=GangChen

2. **LEED Exam Guides series. See the link below:**

   http://www.ArchiteG.com

Note: Other books in the **LEED Exam Guides series** are in the process of being produced. **One book will eventually be produced for each of the LEED exams.** The series include:

LEED AP Exam Guide: *Study Materials, Sample Questions, Mock Exam, Building LEED Certification (LEED NC v2.2), and Going Green,* **Book 1,** LEED Exam Guides series, LEEDSeries.com (Published on 9/23/2008).

LEED GA EXAM GUIDE: *A Must-Have for the LEED Green Associate Exam: Comprehensive Study Materials, Sample Questions, Mock Exam, Green Building LEED Certification, and Sustainability (LEED v3.0),* Book 2, LEED Exam Guide series, ArchiteG.com (Published October 28, 2009)

LEED BD&C EXAM GUIDE: *A Must-Have for the LEED AP BD+C Exam: Comprehensive Study Materials, Sample Questions, Mock Exam, Green Building Design and Construction, LEED Certification, and Sustainability (LEED v3.0),* Book 3, LEED Exam Guide series, ArchiteG.com (Published December 18, 2009)

LEED ID&C EXAM GUIDE: *A Must-Have for the LEED AP ID+C Exam: Comprehensive Study Materials, Sample Questions, Mock Exam, Green Interior Design and Construction, LEED Certification, and Sustainability,* Book 4, LEED Exam Guide series, ArchiteG.com (Published March 8, 2010)

LEED O&M EXAM GUIDE: *A Must-Have for the LEED AP O+M Exam: Comprehensive Study Materials, Sample Questions, Mock Exam, Green Building Operations and Maintenance, LEED Certification, and Sustainability (LEED v3.0),* Book 5, LEED Exam Guide series, ArchiteG.com

LEED HOMES EXAM GUIDE: *A Must-Have for the LEED AP Homes Exam: Comprehensive Study Materials, Sample Questions, Mock Exam, Green Building LEED Certification, and Sustainability*, Book 6, LEED Exam Guide series, ArchiteG.com

LEED ND EXAM GUIDE: *A Must-Have for the LEED AP Neighborhood Development Exam: Comprehensive Study Materials, Sample Questions, Mock Exam, Green Building LEED Certification, and Sustainability*, Book 7, LEED Exam Guide series, ArchiteG.com

LEED GA MOCK EXAMS: *Questions, Answers, and Explanations: A Must-Have for the LEED Green Associate Exam, Green Building LEED Certification, and Sustainability*, Book 8, LEED Exam Guide series, ArchiteG.com (Published August 6, 2010)

LEED O&M MOCK EXAMS: *Questions, Answers, and Explanations: A Must-Have for the LEED O&M Exam, Green Building LEED Certification, and Sustainability*, Book 9, LEED Exam Guide series, ArchiteG.com (Published September 28, 2010)

How to order these books:

You can order them at

http://outskirtspress.com/agent.php?key=11011&page=examguide

or

http://Amazon.com

or

any other Amazon site, such as http://amazon.ca, http://amazon.co.uk, http:// amazon.co.jp, http://amazon.fr, or http:// amazon.de

or

http://bn.com

Following are some detailed descriptions:

LEED Exam Guides series: Comprehensive Study Materials, Sample Questions, Mock Exam, Building LEED Certification and Going Green

LEED (Leadership in Energy and Environmental Design) is the most important trend of development, and it is revolutionizing the construction industry. It has gained tremendous momentum and has a profound impact on our environment.

From LEED Exam Guides series, you will learn how to

1. Pass the LEED Green Associate Exam and various LEED AP + exams (each book will help you with a specific LEED exam).

2. Register and certify a building for LEED certification.

3. Understand the intent for each LEED prerequisite and credit.

4. Calculate points for a LEED credit.

5. Identify the responsible party for each prerequisite and credit.

6. Earn extra credit (exemplary performance) for LEED.

7. Implement the local codes and building standards for prerequisites and credit.

8. Receive points for categories not yet clearly defined by USGBC.

There is currently NO official book on the LEED Green Associate Exam, and most of the existing books on LEED and LEED AP are too expensive and too complicated to be practical and helpful. The pocket guides in LEED Exam Guides series fill in the blanks, demystify LEED, and uncover the tips, codes, and jargon for LEED as well as the true meaning of "going green." They will set up a solid foundation and fundamental framework of LEED for you. Each book in the LEED Exam Guides series covers every aspect of one or more specific LEED rating system(s) in plain and concise language and makes this information understandable to all people.

These pocket guides are small and easy to carry around. You can read them whenever you have a few extra minutes. They are indispensable books for all people— administrators; developers; contractors; architects; landscape architects; civil, mechanical, electrical, and plumbing engineers; interns; drafters; designers; and other design professionals.

Why is the LEED Exam Guides series Needed?

A number of books are available that you can use to prepare for the LEED Exams:

1. *USGBC Reference Guides*. You need to select the correct version of the *Reference Guide* for your exam.

   The *USGBC Reference Guides* are comprehensive, but they give too much information. For example, *The LEED 2009 Reference Guide for Green Building Design and Construction (BD&C)* has about 700 oversized pages. Many of the calculations in the books are too detailed for the exam. They are also expensive (approximately $200 each, so most people may not buy them for their personal use, but instead, will seek to share an office copy).

It is good to read a reference guide from cover to cover if you have the time. The problem is not too many people have time to read the whole reference guide. Even if you do read the whole guide, you may not remember the important issues to pass the LEED exam. You need to reread the material several times before you can remember much of it.

Reading the reference guide from cover to cover without a guidebook is a difficult and inefficient way of preparing for the LEED AP Exam, because you do NOT know what USGBC and GBCI are looking for in the exam.

2. The USGBC workshops and related handouts are concise, but they do not cover extra credits (exemplary performance). The workshops are expensive, costing approximately $450 each.

3. Various books published by a third party are available on Amazon. However, most of them are not very helpful.

There are many books on LEED, but not all are useful.

LEED Exam Guides series will fill in the blanks and become a valuable, reliable source:

a. They will give you more information for your money. Each of the books in the LEED Exam Guides series has more information than the related USGBC workshops.

b. They are exam-oriented and more effective than the USGBC reference guides.

c. They are better than most, if not all, of the other third-party books. They give you comprehensive study materials, sample questions and answers, mock exams and answers, and critical information on building LEED certification and going green. Other third-party books only give you a fraction of the information.

d. They are comprehensive yet concise. They are small and easy to carry around. You can read them whenever you have a few extra minutes.

e. They are great timesavers. I have highlighted the important information that you need to understand and MEMORIZE. I also make some acronyms and short sentences to help you easily remember the credit names.

It should take you about 1 or 2 weeks of full-time study to pass each of the LEED exams. I have met people who have spent 40 hours to study and passed the exams.

You can find sample texts and other information on the LEED Exam Guides series in customer discussion sections under each of my book's listing on Amazon.

What others are saying about *LEED GA Exam Guide* (Book 2, LEED Exam Guide series):

"Finally! A comprehensive study tool for LEED GA Prep!

"I took the 1-day Green LEED GA course and walked away with a power point binder printed in very small print—which was missing MUCH of the required information (although I didn't know it at the time). I studied my little heart out and took the test, only to fail it by 1 point. Turns out I did NOT study all the material I needed to in order to pass the test. I found this book, read it, marked it up, retook the test, and passed it with a 95%. Look, we all know the LEED GA exam is new and the resources for study are VERY limited. This one's the VERY best out there right now. I highly recommend it."
—ConsultantVA

"Complete overview for the LEED GA exam

"I studied this book for about 3 days and passed the exam ... if you are truly interested in learning about the LEED system and green building design, this is a great place to start."
—K.A. Evans

"A Wonderful Guide for the LEED GA Exam

"After deciding to take the LEED Green Associate exam, I started to look for the best possible study materials and resources. From what I thought would be a relatively easy task, it turned into a tedious endeavor. I realized that there are vast amounts of third-party guides and handbooks. Since the official sites offer little to no help, it became clear to me that my best chance to succeed and pass this exam would be to find the most comprehensive study guide that would not only teach me the topics, but would also give me a great background and understanding of what LEED actually is. Once I stumbled upon Mr. Chen's book, all my needs were answered. This is a great study guide that will give the reader the most complete view of the LEED exam and all that it entails.

"The book is written in an easy-to-understand language and brings up great examples, tying the material to the real world. The information is presented in a coherent and logical way, which optimizes the learning process and does not go into details that will not be needed for the LEED Green Associate Exam, as many other guides do. This book stays dead on topic and keeps the reader interested in the material.

"I highly recommend this book to anyone that is considering the LEED Green Associate Exam. I learned a great deal from this guide, and I am feeling very confident about my chances for passing my upcoming exam."
—Pavel Geystrin

"Easy to read, easy to understand

"I have read through the book once and found it to be the perfect study guide for me. The author does a great job of helping you get into the right frame of mind for the content of the exam. I had started by studying the Green Building Design and Construction reference guide for LEED projects produced by the USGBC. That was the wrong approach, simply too much information with very little retention. At 636 pages in textbook format, it would have been a daunting task to get through it. Gang Chen breaks down the points, helping to minimize the amount of information but maximizing the content I was able to absorb. I plan on going through the book a few more times, and I now believe I have the right information to pass the LEED Green Associate Exam."
—Brian Hochstein

"All in one—LEED GA prep material

"Since the LEED Green Associate exam is a newer addition by USGBC, there is not much information regarding study material for this exam. When I started looking around for material, I got really confused about what material I should buy. This LEED GA guide by Gang Chen is an answer to all my worries! It is a very precise book with lots of information, like how to approach the exam, what to study and what to skip, links to on-line material, and tips and tricks for passing the exam. It is like the 'one stop shop' for the LEED Green Associate Exam. I think this book can also be a good reference guide for green building professionals. A must-have!"
—SwatiD

"An ESSENTIAL LEED GA Exam Reference Guide

"This book is an invaluable tool in preparation for the LEED Green Associate (GA) Exam. As a practicing professional in the consulting realm, I found this book to be all-inclusive of the preparatory material needed for sitting the exam. The information provides clarity to the fundamental and advanced concepts of what LEED aims to achieve. A tremendous benefit is the connectivity of the concepts with real-world applications.

"The author, Gang Chen, provides a vast amount of knowledge in a very clear, concise, and logical media. For those that have not picked up a textbook in a while, it is very manageable to extract the needed information from this book. If you are taking the exam, do yourself a favor and purchase a copy of this great guide. Applicable fields: Civil Engineering, Architectural Design, MEP, and General Land Development."
—Edwin L. Tamang

Planting Design Illustrated

One of the most significant books on landscaping!

This is one of the most comprehensive books on planting design. It fills in the blanks in this field and introduces poetry, painting, and symbolism into planting design. It covers in detail the two major systems in planting design: formal planting design and naturalistic planting design. It has numerous line drawings and photos to illustrate the planting design concepts and principles. Through in-depth discussions of historical precedents and practical case studies, it uncovers the fundamental design principles and concepts, as well as underpinning philosophy for planting design. It is an indispensable reference book for landscape architecture students, designers, architects, urban planners, and ordinary garden lovers.

What Others Are Saying About *Planting Design Illustrated* …

"I found this book to be absolutely fascinating. You will need to concentrate while reading it, but the effort will be well worth your time."
—Bobbie Schwartz, former president of APLD (Association of Professional Landscape Designers) and author of *The Design Puzzle: Putting the Pieces Together.*

"This is a book that you have to read, and it is more than well worth your time. Gang Chen takes you well beyond what you will learn in other books about basic principles like color, texture, and mass."
—Jane Berger, editor & publisher of gardendesignonline

"As a long-time consumer of gardening books, I am impressed with Gang Chen's inclusion of new information on planting design theory for Chinese and Japanese gardens. Many gardening books discuss the beauty of Japanese gardens, and a few discuss the unique charms of Chinese gardens, but this one explains how Japanese and Chinese history, as well as geography and artistic traditions, bear on the development of each country's style. The material on traditional Western garden planting is thorough and inspiring, too. *Planting Design Illustrated* definitely rewards repeated reading and study. Any garden designer will read it with profit."
—Jan Whitner, editor of the *Washington Park Arboretum Bulletin*

"Enhanced with an annotated bibliography and informative appendices, *Planting Design Illustrated* offers an especially "reader friendly" and practical guide that makes it a very strongly recommended addition to personal, professional, academic, and community library gardening & landscaping reference collection and supplemental reading list."
—Midwest Book Review

"Where to start? *Planting Design Illustrated* is, above all, fascinating and refreshing! Not something the lay reader encounters every day, the book presents an unlikely topic in an easily digestible, easy-to-follow way. It is superbly organized with a comprehensive table of contents, bibliography, and appendices. The writing, though expertly informative, maintains its accessibility throughout and is a joy to read. The detailed and beautiful illustrations expanding on the concepts presented were my favorite portion. One of the finest books I've encountered in this contest in the past 5 years."

—Writer's Digest 16th Annual International Self-Published Book Awards Judge's Commentary

"The work in my view has incredible application to planting design generally and a system approach to what is a very difficult subject to teach, at least in my experience. Also featured is a very beautiful philosophy of garden design principles bordering poetry. It's my strong conviction that this work needs to see the light of day by being published for the use of professionals, students & garden enthusiasts."

—Donald C Brinkerhoff, FASLA, chairman and CEO of Lifescapes International, Inc.

Index

Made in the USA
Lexington, KY
26 July 2012